REMEMBERING OLUWALE: AN ANTHOLOGY

Remembering Oluwale

An Anthology

edited by
SJ Bradley

with an introduction by
Max Farrar

Valley Press

First published in 2016 by Valley Press
Woodend, The Crescent, Scarborough, YO11 2PW
www.valleypressuk.com

First edition, first printing (May 2016)

ISBN 978-1-908853-71-4
Cat. no. VP0088

Printed and bound in Great Britain by
Charlesworth Press, Wakefield

This anthology is an initiative of the David Oluwale
Memorial Association (charity reg.1151426) in partnership with
Fictions of Every Kind and the Big Bookend Festival.

Contents

Acknowledgements

'from *The Hounding of David Oluwale*' was previously published in Aspden, Kester, *The Hounding of David Oluwale* (London: Vintage, 2008)

'from *Northern Lights*' was previously published in Phillips, Caryl, *Foreigners: Three English Lives* (London: Harvill Secker, 2007)

'Return' by Sai Murray was previously published by Platform as part of a commemorative fold-out poster for Action Saro-Wiwa, designed by Jon Daniel and featuring artwork by Alfredo Jaar. The poem was first performed at 'Dance the Guns to Silence II' on 10th November 2015, at Rich Mix, London, marking twenty years since the execution of the Ogoni 9.

Ian Duhig's poems were written for use in an earlier phase of the David Oluwale memorial campaign and subsequently appeared in *Pandorama* (London: Picador, 2010)

'Time Come' was previously published in Johnson, Linton Kwesi, *Selected Poems* (London: Penguin, 2006)

'A Letter for Mama Oluwale' by Zodwa Nyoni was adapted from the Leeds Young Authors team piece 'Golly Gosh Oluwale Gone,' performed at the opening night of *The Hounding of David Oluwale* at the West Yorkshire Playhouse in 2009. This version was first performed at Britain On Trial: Young Voices Speak Out! at the Carriageworks Theatre, Leeds, on 29th October 2011, organised by Voices that Shake!, Leeds Young Authors, Leeds University MA Activism and Social Change, and a part of the ESRC Festival of Social Science.

Praise from the judges of the Remember Oluwale Writing Prize

'In Claudia Rankine's poem 'Citizen' the speaker is asked in England if she will write about Mark Duggan. She replies "Why don't you?"

Our competition entrants rose to that challenge over David Oluwale's story and its continuing echoes for our society in new and moving ways. Their work stands confidently beside that of better-known writers in an anthology all can be proud of, a document of their refusal to be silent in the face of abusive power.'

IAN DUHIG

Forward Poetry Prize winner and T.S. Eliot Prize shortlistee. His most recent collection is Pandorama.

'I was amazed how this haunting story from almost 50 years ago still has the power to move and to inspire a younger generation of writers. The fine pieces in this anthology show just how much it resonates with issues that continue to trouble us today.'

MARINA LEWYCKA

Author of A Short History of Tractors in Ukrainian *and most recently* The Lubetkin Legacy.

'The passion and moral urgency informing these new voices gives one hope for the future of both imaginative writing and our society's health.'

CARYL PHILLIPS

Writer, Guggenheim Fellow, and winner of the Martin Luther King Memorial Prize. His most recent novel is The Lost Child.

Introduction

MAX FARRAR

'Subject is not recorded in this country'
Nigerian Interpol (1970)[1]

Nigerian Interpol found no records at all for its Lagos-born British citizen David Oluwale. They had been asked to investigate by Chief Superintendent 'Polly' Perkins after Oluwale had been found drowned in the River Aire in Leeds, UK on 4th May 1969. Had Gary Galvin, a young Leeds police cadet, not suspected that David had been killed by two of his superior officers, David's only written records in the UK would have been those kept by the police, the courts, the prisons, the hospitals and the rudimentary welfare services that knew him. This book is one of an accumulating number of publications, in all genres, which are offering a more respectful and analytical response to David's difficult time in the north of England.

This book results from the Oluwale Writing Prize, set up by the David Oluwale Memorial Association (DOMA) in partnership with Leeds-based projects The Leeds Big Bookend and Fictions of Every Kind. Writing is important to the DOMA for several reasons. The charity's short name, 'Remember Oluwale', is taken from those two words painted in huge white capitals on a grimy Yorkshire stone wall on Chapeltown Road in 1971. This is the year that two officers were convicted of assaulting David, but acquitted of his manslaughter. Chapeltown is the neighbourhood of Leeds in which, at that time, the majority of British citizens of African, Caribbean and South Asian descent lived. Those fifteen letters on the wall — reflecting the hurt and outrage felt among the black populations and progressive whites of Leeds — were the shortest and most poignant of the written responses to David's harsh life

---

[1] Aspden, 2008, p. 42

and terrible death. It was this graffiti that first alerted me to David Oluwale. Writing plays an essential part in the process through which pain and anger are examined, translated and, sometimes, healed.

Leeds-based newspapers wrote extensively about the trial of Inspector Ellerker and Sergeant Kitching, which lasted for fifteen days in November 1971. They were accused of actual and grievous bodily harm against David Oluwale, and his manslaughter. The papers picked over some of the evidence meticulously assembled by Perkins and his team from London's Metropolitan police. The pure cruelty of Ellerker and Kitching, exposed by several other Leeds police officers, made dramatic headlines.

But it took two professional writers over the next few years to reflect in more detail on David's life and death. Their work laid the basis for changes in social and political policy on what today we refer to as 'the Oluwale issues': migration, racism, homelessness, mental ill-health, destitution, police malpractice and incarceration.

Shortly after the trial, the British-Guyanese writer Ron Phillips wrote a long article for the liberal monthly magazine *Race Today* titled 'One Lame Darkie.' This was the expression used in the trial to describe David. He had limped and shuffled through the streets of Leeds during his periods outside prison or psychiatric hospital, spending his last two years sleeping rough in the city centre, where he fell under two policemen's boots and truncheons. Phillips, like the writer of the graffiti, an advocate of Black Power, might have upset some of his readers with this analysis of David's plight:

> [T]he destruction of David Oluwale represented the inevitable result of contact between a powerful institution and a powerless individual, where that individual is defined as threatening or superfluous ... If Ellerker and Kitching did chase or throw David Oluwale into the river Aire, they would have been acting, as they saw it, in defence of a society which defines black people as a threat.
>
> (Phillips, 1972, p. 18)

Two years later Jeremy Sandford, a white upper-class man whose work was marked by his sympathy for the homeless (*Cathy*

Come Home was his most famous script) produced a radio play for the BBC titled *Smiling David*. Sandford never shied from the terrible crimes against David, where 'crime' covers both actual violence and the tacit violence of social neglect. But Sandford presented David as an excellent dancer and a good-time man, always smiling, at least until he was sent into Menston psychiatric hospital (from 1953 to 1961). He got this picture from Maureen Baker, the Irish-born activist whose entire career was devoted to anti-racist work, who recalled meeting David and caring for him. Maureen, as her daughter Abi put it to me, had a good memory and a 'fable memory', and Sandford's version of her account cannot be completely relied upon. We'd like to think of him as smiling David. But in remembering David, we remember what a trickster memory can be (Farrar, 2015).

During the 1970s writing about David appeared in football chants at Leeds United's home ground. To the tune of 'My Old Man', Leeds fans would sing:

> Policeman said 'Get in the van,
> Don't dilly dally on the way'
> They had him in the van and in half a minute
> They were down by the river and they chucked him in it
> Cos he dillied and he dallied, dallied and dillied
> Lost his way and dint know where to roam
> And you can't trust a copper if your name is Oluwale
> When you can't find your way home

> (Aspden, 2008, p. 195)

The poet Linton Kwesi Johnson, while a member of the radical collective editing a new-look *Race Today*, now following the Marxist philosophy of CLR James, also wrote and performed about David in the 1970s . Like the Leeds fans, Johnson is convinced that the two policemen murdered David. Linton Kwesi Johnson has kindly allowed us to reprint in this book one of his early poems — read it on page 41 with a dub reggae beat in your head.

We had to wait until the early 21st century for two other writers to publish their detailed research into David's case, made possible by the release of court papers under the 30-year rule.

Kester Aspden's book in its first edition (2007) took its title from a derogatory word used to describe David in a police record sheet: *Nationality: Wog*. Thankfully, 'wog' is a term you don't hear much these days. Current throughout the 1950s, '60s and '70s, it was the equivalent of the term euphemistically referred to as the 'N word.' In the second edition the book was re-titled *The Hounding of David Oluwale*. Everyone interested in writing will ponder on that word 'hounding.' It was carefully chosen by the prosecution barrister because it left open for the jury to decide whether the police officers charged with assault and manslaughter actually pushed David into the River Aire. A witness said he had seen two men in uniform pursuing a limping old man down a side-street off The Calls in the city centre, beside Leeds Bridge. But Judge Hinchcliffe refused to let the jury make up its mind whether Ellerker and Kitching had 'hounded' David to his death. He ruled that the witness was not sufficiently precise for the jury to be allowed to consider the manslaughter charge.

Aspden deployed his skills as an academic historian to the highest standard. No dry catalogue of facts, he crafted a terse literary style that owes something to David Peace's prose. (Peace's quartet of books about Leeds in the 1970s, when David Sutcliffe — the so-called Yorkshire Ripper — was at large, provide another series of insights into the worst aspects of Leeds life in this period.) We are very grateful to Kester Aspden for permission to reprint a section from his book (see pages 23-30). Aspden's extract explains some of the investigatory work done by Perkins and his team and, crucially, provides compelling detail of the state of 'race relations' in the city of Leeds at the time of David's death.

A very different type of writing about David appeared, coincidentally, in 2007. A third of Caryl Phillips's *Foreigners: Three English Lives*, titled 'Northern Lights,' is devoted to David's life and death. This is remarkable for its possibly unique juxtaposition of imaginative writing, transcripts of 'welfare' records from the archives, economic history of Leeds, interviews with people who knew David, an email, and a searing interpretation of David's life. Phillips was born in St Kitts but grew up in Leeds. As a young black teenager he walked the very streets on which David was hounded, and experienced racism and unwanted attention from the police in Leeds. He paints a picture of David as a man of integrity and resistance: someone who steadfastly refused to be disappeared from the city, despite the impossible odds stacked against him. While this is not the 'smiling David' of Maureen Baker's account, it is a man who — known to his friends in the early 1950s as Yankee, such was his delight in American culture — is not to be pigeonholed as a victim. Phillips' interview with one of David's Nigerian friends, who knew him while he did hard labouring work in Sheffield, appears on pages 31-32, and we thank Caryl Phillips for permission to reprint. It was Phillips' suggestion that there should be a memorial to David in the city of Leeds that stimulated the Remember Oluwale charity's formation.

Ian Duhig has also kindly given us permission to reprint his poems reflecting on David's life and death (pages 36-40) and Zodwa Nyoni has allowed us to reprint her lament for David's mother (pages 43-44). Duhig, of Irish heritage, worked with the homeless for many years in Leeds and was even employed at Hepworths in 1974 where Kitching, recently released from prison, was the malevolent head of security. Like Duhig, Nyoni, a refugee from Zimbabwe, understands the contemporary relevance of David's story, as new migrants face a similar plight: exploited at work, if they can find it, on low wages or none at all, so destitution stares them in the face, mentally traumatised by their experiences, and often homeless or shifting from sofa to sofa. Another reprint for which we are grateful comes from Sai Murray, a poet who is a member of the Board of the Remember Oluwale charity. This connects David's story to that of Ken Saro-Wiwa, another Nigerian whose memory is being kept alive by art and activism (see page 33). The texts we have received from members of The Baggage Handlers (pages 45-57) are especially important to us, because these formed part of a memorable performance, launching the charity, at night in January 2013, in the freezing cold, on the ground that we hope will soon become a memorial garden for David, next to the River Aire and close to the point he was forced into the water.

The David Oluwale Memorial Association exists not only to keep alive the story of David's dark days in Leeds, but to educate and campaign on the persistence today of the very same issues that David endured. The charity applauds the progress the city has made since David's time, and it enthusiastically supports the aim of its leader, Cllr Judith Blake (2015-6), to make Leeds 'a compassionate, caring' city where everyone is welcome, and greater equality is achieved. The Oluwale Memorial Garden, beside the River Aire, close to where David was drowned, will be a place which embodies all the city's aspirations, and more. It will be a dynamic space where everyone in Leeds will be able to share food, have conversations and enjoy culture from all over the world. While never minimising the gruesome aspects of the Oluwale saga, or criticising those writers who remind us of grim and gritty Leeds, the charity aims to make a place of hope, growth and succour close to the very place where David died. To build that hope, the charity uses performance and creative art as one means of communicating its ideals. The garden will host a specially commissioned sculpture by a world-renowned artist, enhancing the city's ambition to be the European Capital of Culture in 2023.

It is in this spirit that we initiated the Oluwale Writing Prize. We wanted new stories and poems that would creatively reflect on David's life and death, and pick up on the manifold issues his story represents. The new stories and poems selected here do just that. While some respond to David as a Nigerian, others note that destitution knows no national boundaries, nor gender, nor colour, and encourage us to empathise with the plight of all those who have been pushed to the margins of society. In one we feel for the child of a homeless woman, and perhaps wonder if there is any truth in the claim that Kester Aspden encountered (and repeated in Sandford's play): that David had a partner and perhaps some children. Aspden found no evidence, but as one of the poems here points out, the most excluded leave few records. Our theme of writing, making a mark, is picked up in a poem placing a man breathing on the window of a restaurant so he can make words in the mist. All the words in this volume do that essential work of empathetically entering the world of others, helping us understand, and — as DOMA advocates — propelling us to make changes.

Our partners in the Oluwale Writing Prize — Fiona Gell at the Leeds Big Bookend, and SJ Bradley of Fictions of Every Kind — have been assiduous and wonderfully efficient; we are utterly grateful to them. Sarah has been ably assisted by Jenna Isherwood, Claire Stephenson, Nasser Hussain, and Becky Cherriman in first-reading all the materials submitted. We thank them very much indeed. Our publisher, Valley Press, has been wonderfully helpful. We are immensely grateful to our judges, the renowned writers Ian Duhig, Marina Lewycka and Caryl Phillips for so readily agreeing to lend their prestige to our competition.

We are sure you will enjoy and benefit from all the stories and poems in this book. Please follow all of us — Remember Oluwale, Leeds Big Bookend and Fictions of Every Kind — on social media, and provide us with any feedback you may have.

Max Farrar
Secretary, David Oluwale Memorial Association (DOMA)
Leeds, April 2016

REFERENCES

Aspden, Kester (2008), *The Hounding of David Oluwale*, London: Vintage
Blake, Judith (2015-6), 'Leeds City Council Summary Best Council Plan 2015-20. Update 2015-6' published at http://www.leeds.gov.uk/docs/Best%20Council%20Plan%20Summary%2015-20%20v1.1.pdf [Accessed 22.3.16]
Farrar, Max (2015), 'Remembering Oluwale — Re-presenting the life and death in Leeds, UK, of a destitute British Nigerian' Available at http://www.rememberoluwale.org/david-oluwale/remembering-david-in-history-poetry-music-and-film/ [Accessed 22.3.16]
Phillips, Caryl (2007), *Foreigners: Three English Lives*, London: Harwill Secker
Phillips, Ron (1972), 'One Lame Darkie' in *Race Today*, January Available at http://www.rememberoluwale.org/wp-content/uploads/2012/06/Ron-Phillips-Race-Today-1972.pdf [Accessed 22.3.16]
Sandford, Jeremy (1974), *Smiling David*, London: Calder and Boyars

A note from the editor
& contest organiser

SJ BRADLEY

When Max Farrar of the Remember Oluwale charity first approached me to organise and edit an anthology in memory of David Oluwale, I quickly said yes. I knew that the foundation in David's name worked to challenge issues of marginalisation, racism, homelessness, and mental ill health in our cities. As somebody who has been a writer, an organiser in arts activism in Leeds, and a worker in mental health settings, these were certainly issues I had encountered many times second-hand through my work.

In Kester Aspden's harrowing but necessary book, *The Hounding of David Oluwale*, the author sets out the context of Leeds in the 1960s, and how David, a homeless and dispossessed man, could be assaulted, taunted, and hounded by two police officers senior in the force. Eventually David, who faced these assaults with bravery and courage, was found floating dead in the River Aire. This was a shameful episode in Leeds history, and I recommend reading Aspden's book to find out more about David's story. We are very thankful to have Aspden's permission to republish an excerpt from the book here.

We are also very pleased to have been able to gain permission to republish previously existing works by Linton Kwesi Johnson, Ian Duhig, Caryl Phillips, Zodwa Nyoni, and Sai Murray; also, work by The Baggage Handlers, a project facilitated by writer Rommi Smith. One of our aims was to produce a literary artefact of much of the work inspired by and written about David, and I hope this is something we have managed to achieve.

One way that we can bring 'David's issues' to the fore and keep his story alive, is by keeping on writing about him, keeping on saying his name, and keeping on telling his story. To this end, we ran the Remember Oluwale Writing Prize, and entrants took up the challenge with aplomb. During the course of the contest we received 70 entries, all of which tackled 'David's issues' with huge passion and inventiveness. In this book, you'll see the very best of the stories and poems we received.

In Ian Harker's 'Aire,' a prize-winner, the lonely ending of David's life is explored. In 'The Weight of a Life' by Stephen Whiting and 'Promises' by Gloria Dawson, writers explore the value of life: who does society deem to have importance, and who gets left out? This theme of dispossession and dehumanisation is further explored by Wes Lee in her beautiful poem, 'The Story has Overtaken Me,' in Rachel Bowers' 'Coppers,' and in Rob Miles' 'Zones of Exclusion.' 'Do not hate me for magenta hands: they are your hands too,' Bowers writes. Entrants did not forget to write about the hope contained within aspects of David's story, and there is some optimism in Char March's poem, 'Son of the mother-whose-children-are-like-fish,' another prize-winner.

We have included several true stories from the modern day about immigration and asylum seeking in the UK. In Kojeyo Adebakin's 'In the Cold,' we read of a family facing eviction and homelessness. In David Cundall's 'Signs and Wonders,' a man facing deportation by the UK Border Agency tries to gain a last minute reprieve through legal means, whilst in 'i.m.B.B,' Ian Fairley implores us not to forget those systematically excluded from society: "I was not born to be a ghost."

The importance of remembering and memorialising David is tackled more directly in Chérie Taylor-Battiste's vocal poem,"He Remains.' Taylor-Battiste told me in an email: 'I saw the narrative voice as a Yoruba Egungun spirit, summoned by families for protection and guidance. So the voice was a sort of "witnessing presence" to the abuse, that was only enabled, by the fact that nobody saw it. They also believe the ultimate reward for getting to the afterlife is to be remembered, to have your life in the oral tales of your community. So the ancestor was whispering in the ear of his community, but also in our ears, ensuring [...] that we "Remember Oluwale."'

Running the Remember Oluwale Writing Prize was something of a group endeavour, and wouldn't have happened without the enthusiastic help and support of the following people. Fiona Gell of the Big Bookend was hugely enthusiastic, very well organized, and provided a lot of help and support to the contest, including hosting it on the Big Bookend website. Without her help, this book would not exist. Max Farrar of Remember Oluwale suggested the whole thing in the first place, and also recruited a stellar team of judges: Ian Duhig, Marina Lewycka, and Caryl Phillips, without whom we would have not had such a high calibre of entries. All of our judges agreed to read the shortlisted entries voluntarily, in support of Remember Oluwale's work, and for that, we can't thank them enough. Max Farrar was also the person who sourced, and gained the relevant permissions, to republish previously existing works in this book. Huge thanks also go to Sai Murray for his support in this endeavour, for sourcing work from The Baggage Handlers, and also for his work on designing the front cover. We are also very grateful to Valley Press for publishing this book, and for their support.

There was also a great deal of work behind the scenes as contest entries came in. There were far too many for one person to read alone, and give them the attention they deserved. We had an excellent team of filter readers who blind-read entries as they came in: huge thanks to Nasser Hussain, Becky Cherriman, and to my Fictions of Every Kind co-organizers Jenna Isherwood and Claire Stephenson, for doing this. I am also grateful to my Fictions co-organisers for providing a second read, and suggestions during the editorial process, as I put the book together. Previously published and performed works appear in the first section of the book, with contest entries responding to David's life appearing afterwards.

Some of the contest entries were previously published: 'Stephen Lawrence Isn't on the National Curriculum' also appears in Josephine Corcoran's pamphlet *The Misplaced House*; an earlier version of 'Summer in Winter' by Rachel Fenton was previously published in *Eclectic Flash #1*; Rob Miles' 'Zones of Exclusion' was previously published in *Militant Thistles*, and a slightly different version of Catherine Vallely's 'A Friendship Apart' was first self-published by the Fermamagh Writers.

Finally, my thanks to you for picking up this book. I hope it will encourage you to read more about David's story, and to keep on telling it.

SJ Bradley, March 2016

from *The Hounding of David Oluwale*

KESTER ASPDEN

This excerpt, taken from the chapter 'North,' provides some context on the charging of two police officers accused of David Oluwale's assault and manslaughter. One of the defendants, Ellerker, had formerly been an Inspector in the Leeds City Police, but had been found guilty of misconduct as an officer of justice and sentenced to nine months in jail, for assisting in the attempted cover-up of a death caused by a colleague who was drunk at the wheel of his car. The following extract, republished here with the kind permission of the author Kester Aspden and the publishers, Vintage, continues on from this point.

The fact that Ellerker was convicted, and therefore to some degree discredited, made it arguably easier for the officers in the Oluwale investigation to break rank. It was possibly for this reason that Polly Perkins was able to build a case against Ellerker and Kitching.

The investigation into Oluwale's death began while the conspiracy trial at Leeds Assizes was in progress. At that stage, Oluwale was still something of a joke – in death as in life. 'The Kitching Sink Drama,' that was one of the jokes. At a practice of the Leeds City Police band someone suggested adding 'The Deep River Rhapsody' and 'The Oluwale Chorus' to their repertoire.

The investigation involved wide questioning of officers throughout Leeds City Police, but Polly Perkins and Haddrell directed most attention at those on Ellerker and Kitching's shift – 'Ken Kitching's Deep River Boys', as they were now known. Polly and Haddrell didn't run up against the complete wall of silence they had half expected. Some officers co-operated out of self-interest, fearing disciplinary proceeding and worse if they didn't. PC Keith Seager was formally interviewed ten times — about twenty hours of questioning in total. One of Seager's colleagues recalled seeing him at the Magistrates' Court: he had lost weight and looked drawn; he was anxious that he was facing disciplinary action and possible criminal charges. PC Gary Briggs gave statements on 28 October, 17 November, 23 November, 24 November, 15 December 1970. His penultimate statement begins: 'I now want to tell you the whole truth about what happened in the car when I was taking Mr Ellerker up to John Peters in Lands Lane.' The truth was slowly and painfully wrung from very reluctant witnesses.

Those who broke the code of loyalty could expect pariah status. Millgarth officers would have had in mind the two traffic policemen who had given evidence at the 'Leeds Police Trial.' Certain officers who were helping the investigation were shipped out of Millgarth to other sub-divisions. When Brian Topp was transferred to Dewsbury Road on 6 November nobody would talk to him – it was as if a leper was in their midst, he told me.

The most important task for the Oluwale investigation was to establish when the alleged John Peters incident could have taken place. It was discovered that Oluwale had signed on for his dole on 16 April 1968. This narrowed the timeframe of the investigation. The duty books of Millgarth officers were scrutinised. Polly became interested in the night of 17/18 April 1969.

A postman came forward in response to the press appeal with some interesting information. He said he was on his way home on the bus one early morning when he saw police vehicles by the river at Warehouse Hill. He thought that it was around the time the body of Oluwale was pulled from the Aire. He also recalled having a conversation with the bus conductor, who told him that he had just seen two policemen chasing someone down Call Lane to the river. The postman didn't think any more about it, he explained to detectives. Detectives examined the postman's rota and established that the incident had probably taken place on the early morning of 18 April 1969. When the bus conductor was eventually traced his statement appeared to confirm what the postman had said.

In the course of the investigation, allegations were made of other assaults on Oluwale going back to August 1968. Polly and Haddrell heard that Ellerker and Kitching hounded the man.

[Police] Cadet Gary Galvin, the youth who'd set the whole investigation off, was an isolated figure. But he was toughing it out.

5 November. Gazzer [Galvin] should have been at one of the great south Leeds bonfires; instead he was up in front of Scotland Yard's murder squad at Brotherton House. Polly asked him why he thought Oluwale had ended up in the river. Gazzer replied that he'd possibly been pushed in 'because he was coloured and there is racial prejudice everywhere.' It was just his personal opinion, he said.

Whilst digging into David Oluwale's antecedent history, the investigation team turned up a couple of documents: two innocuous-looking Leeds City Police charge sheets. Oluwale had picked up many of them during the last few months of his life. These two dated from 23 February 1969 and 11 March 1969. There was space on these forms for various details: name, date of birth, address (by this time Oluwale was always N.F.A.[No Fixed Abode]) sex, marital status, etc. There was also a space for the nationality of the prisoner. On the first charge sheet 'BRIT' had been typed in under NAT, but had then been crossed out by hand and 'WOG' scrawled instead. On the second charge sheet, a few weeks later, no alterations had been made. It was simply typed to read NAT: WOG.

* * *

The racial politics of David Oluwale ran alongside the criminal investigation. Leeds City Police was fortunate in that it had a skilled politician in its deputy chief constable. It was Austin Haywood who tried to ensure that the Oluwale case did not develop into a catastrophe.

The man responsible for discipline in the force would never be loved. Haywood even looked like a bringer of bad news. His face was narrow, thin and bloodless; a frugal eater, he remained as stick-thin as he was in his younger days. With his dark suits and dark hair his look was funereal. He fancied himself as something of an academic authority on the finer points of police discipline. Nothing mattered to Haywood more than the good name of his force.

Leeds City Police had a long and proud history going back to 1836, but by the late 1960s it was a threatened institution. Following the amalgamations of other Yorkshire forces in 1968, there was talk of disbanding the Leeds and Bradford city forces and merging them with the West Yorkshire Constabulary. Leeds City Police was resisting, trying to persuade the Home Office that it was a large city with a large enough policing establishment (1,300 officers) to justify its separate existence. However, its case had not been helped by a number of damaging criminal cases involving its officers. The corruption trial at Leeds Assizes came on top of other recent criminal prosecutions of Leeds police officers, some for petty thefts, others more serious. The most serious involved an entire shift in the Ireland Wood sub-division which led to a sergeant and a number of his officers receiving prison sentences for theft. But Haywood knew that these were nothing compared to the damage Oluwale could bring.

Racism had loomed larger in the city's mind since Enoch Powell's 'Rivers of Blood' speech in April 1968. But there was a happy delusion in Leeds that it was too moderate, too phlegmatic in character for race hatred. In the council there was agreement that Leeds didn't need to invest, as other local authorities had done, in a community relations officer — and it hadn't. And then came Burley, July 1969.

Violent disturbances broke out in the Burley Lodge area [of Leeds] on two successive nights after nineteen-year old Kenny Horsfall was stabbed in the head and killed by a young Asian man. The attack followed an argument outside an Indian café in which racial abuse was thrown. The night after the stabbing, a sweltering Sunday, between six and eight hundred white locals spilled out on the streets after closing time. The mob, appalled by the death of one of its own (which had left a young woman widowed), vented their anger on Asian houses and premises. Chants of 'Go home wogs' and 'Get the Pakis' were heard. Women urged their menfolk on. Without a solid show from seventy Leeds City Police officers there could have been lynchings. There was further trouble on the Monday night. Far-right activists were in the area hoping to exploit the situation – but Burley's hatred wasn't ideological, it was tribal. For days the local Asian community was under siege; some gathered up their belongings and fled to Bradford.

The national papers were up to find out what had fired the largest outbreak of anti-immigrant violence post-'Rivers of Blood.' Khan Chaudhry of the Pakistani Muslim Association told a *Sunday Times* journalist, 'I can hardly believe this is England; that I cannot walk through this part of Leeds without fear of my life.' Glen English, a West Indian who came to Leeds after the war, said that Enoch Powell's speech had made it worse for black people: 'Ten years ago nobody bothered about coloured people, now you hear white people saying: "Time they were sent home," and "There's too many."' Reporters found deep resentment against the Asian residents. The indigenous inhabitants of Burley were repelled by their poor hygiene, the smells from their cooking, hated to use the shared outside toilets if they were unlucky enough to live next to them. It used to be single men, doing the dirty jobs. Now their wives were over and they were buying up all the houses and having kids. They'd disturbed the order of their community.

In the Civic Hall and beyond it was said that what happened in Burley was nothing more than 'beer riots.' According to Merlyn Rees, MP for South Leeds and Under-Secretary of State with special responsibility for race relations, when people had too much ale on summer evenings they did silly things. The Lord Mayor declared: 'There is no racial problem in Leeds.' And the police agreed.

But Leeds now looked like a city where race mattered a lot. Diana Phillips, who became Leeds' first black Justice of the Peace in 1967, was on the bench when a number of the Burley rioters appeared before the court requesting bail. Gilbert Parr, the chairman of the bench, advised Phillips that she should stand down in the interests of impartiality. Phillips respectfully submitted. Defence solicitor Ronnie Teeman was amazed: he hadn't even suggested that bias might be an issue. The national press picked up on the story. A

Times editorial deplored Phillips' exclusion. One of the most prominent members of the local West Indian community had been humiliated. Phillips deeply regretted giving in to Parr's request.

Two men were sentenced to life for Kenny Horsfall's murder, and a number of rioters received lengthy prison sentences. Though the activists managed to prise the resources for an immigration liaison officer out of the council, there was a reluctance in the city to see what happened in Burley in July 1969 as anything other than criminal thuggery. There was no soul-searching. Burley was ignored.

Austin Haywood was acutely conscious that a racial controversy would be disastrous for the reputation of Leeds City Police. Though the force had been praised for its robust action in Burley (angry residents taunted the police with comments like 'Why don't you black your faces?'), relations between police and black people in areas of black settlement like Chapeltown had deteriorated. It wasn't just Leeds. Nationally, police-black relations had worsened over the course of the last decade and was becoming the subject of political comment, books and TV documentaries.

Leeds City Police wasn't ignorant of the problems. In 1969 the force appointed four part-time liaison officers to work with immigrants. Probationer constables were lectured on race relations. Pushing this agenda was Leeds's scholarly Assistant Chief Constable, Adrian Clissitt, who had been the recipient of a United Nations Human Rights Fellowship to study the role of the police in the protection of the rights of immigrants in the United States and the Caribbean. And in DC Peter Blakeney, who had been raised and educated in India, it was blessed with somebody who knew Hindi and Urdu and was sensitive to the different cultures — knowledge which, in an increasingly racially-mixed Leeds, the force were happy to utilise.

Yet there had been no progress in Leeds City Police in the recruitment of black police officers. In 1969, with an immigrant population of 7,000 Indians and Pakistanis, 6,000 West Indians and 1,000 Africans, Leeds had not one black police officer (the records of other forces were little better). Few police officers had any understanding of, or sympathy with, the black communities they were serving, and black people didn't recognise themselves in the police. Unpredictable, lazy, noisy, brash, untidy, deceitful, aggressive, excitable, arrogant — this was the stereotype of the black person which the British bobby nursed. Most Leeds bobbies went on calling Chapeltown's International club 'the coon club.'

Haywood had good reason to be anxious about the impact the Oluwale case would have on the police's relations with the black community. It was becoming a more questioning, more radicalised community, with the Black Power movement making its influence felt amongst the young in Leeds around this time. So Haywood began to cultivate those he saw as the influential, responsible figures in the black community. In November 1970, soon after the investigation was opened, Haywood summoned Maureen Baker to Brotherton House. A white Irish woman, Baker had been at the centre of anti-racist campaigns in Leeds and Yorkshire since the days of the Coloured Commonwealth Citizens' Committee in the mid-1950s. Haywood and Maureen Baker struck up an understanding. She'd return to the community and make it known that it was policemen themselves who had exposed the story of David Oluwale, and that Leeds City Police was leaving no stone unturned in the search for the truth. In return, Baker left with a commitment from Haywood to introduce potent measures to improve police-black relations. A few months later the Chief Constable met representatives of the United Caribbean Association. The Leeds Scheme, as it became known, brought rank-and-file policemen into dialogue with ordinary members of the black community, not the activists or self-appointed leaders. Introduced in 1971, it would be commended by a parliamentary select committee as an innovative contribution to improved race relations, one worthy of imitation.

Haywood appeared to Maureen Baker as a concerned reformer looking to adapt policing to changing times and circumstances. But running even deeper within Haywood was the instinct for institutional self-preservation. He wasn't just worried about Chapeltown, a marginal black community; he was also worried about how the Oluwale case would be received by the majority society. Even in these racist times the idea of the law going for a man simply because he was black would have been deeply repugnant to Middle England with its deep conviction that Britain was synonymous with fairness and the rule of law. Even when hostility to immigrants was at its highest pitch — 1969 — a Home Office poll found that Powellite sympathies could co-exist with support for anti-discrimination measures. The attitude seems to have been: we don't really want you here, but since you are here and British citizens in law, you shouldn't be treated like a dog. Haywood knew that if the alleged crimes against Oluwale were seen to be racially-motivated then the case would achieve far greater notoriety. Not just two police officers, but Leeds City Police as an institution would be in the dock. It could spell the force's ruin.

AFTERWORD: *In fact, the trial of Ellerker and Kitching, and the national focus on the deficiencies of the Leeds police, led to steady reform, particularly when the West Yorkshire Police force was established in 1974. Police cadet Gary Galvin later left the police service and became a criminologist. His son, Carl Galvin, is proud of his father's role in exposing Ellerker and Kitching and serves with the West Yorkshire Police.*

from *Northern Lights*

CARYL PHILLIPS

The idea for a memorial in Leeds to David Oluwale came from
Caryl Phillips. It had occurred to him while researching David's
story for the book that would become *Foreigners: Three English
Lives* (2007). This book, as described on Phillips's website, is 'A
hybrid of reportage, fiction, and historical fact that tells the stories
of three black men whose tragic lives speak resoundingly to the
place and role of the foreigner in English society.' The first two
parts set out the lives of Francis Barber, Samuel Johnson's black
assistant, and Randolph Turpin, the black British man who
was world heavyweight boxing champion. The third part, titled
'Northern Lights,' is devoted to David Oluwale. In this extract,
Phillips records one of David's friends' recollections.

I was living in Sheffield when the case went to trial and I thought,
'goodness, I know that guy.' It was David. I was outraged that the
police would target him in the way the newspapers said they did,
and behave with such unbridled brutality. Obviously they had a
personal vendetta against him, but the David I knew was stubborn
and was never a man to back down. I knew he would have refused
to play second-best to these people. David and I first met when we
were about fifteen. We were part of the same group of about six to
ten guys who ran together in Lagos. At Christmas and Easter we
used to dress up in fancy-dress; you know, a cowboy on a bicycle
or something like that. We called ourselves the Odunlami Area
Boys' Club and our dream was to escape to England, for the war
had 'officially' educated us about that place. Olu had an uncle who
ran a hotel called Ilojo Hotel in Tinubu Square, and sometimes we
would meet there. Then eventually, one by one, we all sought out
ships to stowaway on and we made our way to England. I was lucky
for my captain let me work my passage painting the ship, and when

we docked in Birkenhead he handed me over to the immigration officer but he told the man that I'd worked my passage. Eventually I made my way to Yorkshire where I'd heard there were good jobs, and I got work at the Hatfield Steel Works. I couldn't believe it but Olu was also working there. David had the same no-nonsense attitude about him, and I was really very happy to see a face from Lagos, but I worried about him. He wouldn't let anything go. Nobody was going to do this or that to him, and his attitude was always getting him into trouble. If a foreman said something wrong to him it would be, 'fuck off' and there really wasn't any point in talking to him. I tried. I would say, 'Hey, Olu' but he was a stubborn, fighting man who simply found it impossible to back down and work the system. I worried about Olu. We all had strong heads as youngsters in Lagos, but maybe Olu's head was a little stronger. When I heard about the case I felt sick. I was shocked to hear that he had been reduced to sleeping in the street, but I knew that Olu would never back down and let these people humiliate him. Maybe that's it; he was a little stronger and more determined. But I didn't know that he was sleeping in the street. I just didn't know.

Return

Sai Murray is a poet, designer and a founder Board member of
the David Oluwale Memorial Association. He is also a founding
poet facilitator/mentor with Shake! – Platform's youth arts and
activism programme. Platform's work campaigning for social
and ecological justice makes evident the links between the UK
and Nigeria: the links of migration and colonialism; the links
between multi-national oil companies and the decimation of
Niger Delta communities. Action Saro-Wiwa is a Platform project
which marks 20 years since the Nigerian writer and activist Ken
Saro-Wiwa and 8 Ogoni colleagues were hanged by the military
government for campaigning against Shell.

This poem was commissioned by Platform to mark the journey
of the 'Battle Bus' to Nigeria – a living memorial sculpture to
the Ogoni 9 created in solidarity by artist Sokari Douglas Camp.
The Remember Oluwale charity is proud to associate itself with
the memory of Ken and the work of Platform. Read more about
Platform here: http://platformlondon.org/about-us/

The bus ticket reads: "Return"
"Back to where you came from"
How far is this journey for us?
To return to the origin of things?

To return to a time
Before monocrops of concrete and glass
Punched skyward,
Fertilised by Afrikan blood.

This journey begins with libation
A baptism
Of water. Fire. Burning free.
Remoulding. Rising again.

We have been here before:
Ocean and air breathe these deaths
Steel sinews hold muscle memory
Ecosystems oil the engine.

The wheels on the bus go round
And round. Round and round
And crack. And judder.
And round.

Turn. Click. Crunch.
Grate. Burr. Crash. Drive.
Chain. Stroke. Chain. Stroke.
Whip. Whip. Drive.

A night time traffic
Over unpaved pot-holed roads
Directed into blind alleys, open waters.
Overboard. Under board. Above board.

The bus will be departing at…
Some time today… maybe tomorrow.
At earliest convenience
To our decolonised clocks.

Calling at all points from:
Trans-Atlantic Triangle to Black Lives Matter.
Connecting Bristol to Montgomery
to Alexandra to Ogoni.

The wind whispers: "Return"
Head looking backward, the bird flies forward.
We turn.
Back. To where we came from.

from *The Masque of Blankness*

IAN DUHIG

Max Farrar suggested I supply a few notes to this poem which was originally part of a theatrical reading at West Yorkshire Playhouse, linking scenes by other writers such as Rommi Smith reflecting to different aspects of the Oluwale story. Our cast had an array of accents, but one of the advantages of iambic pentameter was it evened out any problems in this area as well as being the rhythm Leeds speakers naturally fall into, according to Tony Harrison. "The Holy City" referred to in the text is an old antisemitic nickname for Leeds due to its significant Jewish population. This tradition of bigotry was evident in contemporary BNP [British National Party] blogs about the David Oluwale Memorial Campaign I monitored, which partially led to the choice to base my piece on Jonson's 'Masque of Blackness' which apart from anything else was used by England's new king, James I, to relaunch "Britain" as a brand the united kingdom might more easily identify with, betraying the fictions behind BNP nationalism. The personifications of rivers in Jonson's masque reminded me of Oshun the water orisa in Ifá and Yoruba religions, syncretized with Our Lady of Charity in Cuba, and the idea of David being received into her arms at the end of his life, somehow come home again in the centre of Leeds, seemed to me appropriate in the memorial that at this stage was itself only an idea.

Ian Duhig, March 2016

… now blankness can speak through me in blank verse
of files official secrets thirty years,
all mention of their content drawing blanks,
of one we blanked in life and dead, did not wake.
Our tale is paradoxographical,
since contradictions are what most defines
This squarèd circle of celestial bodies...
that's from Johnson's masque we're taking off
in memory of David Oluwale,
Saint David on the BNP blog
attacking what this theatre had planned.
He was a paradox, a Christian
and godson of Oceanus and Oshun
whose surname *Oluwale*'s Yoruba,
in English 'God Comes Home' — to God's Own County,
Yorkshire! what could be more right than that?
His last home was our Holy City centre,
final circle of his Christian hell,
a ring that boxed him in from Millgarth's nick
to Armley Gaol and then the NHS
that locked him up a decade, did no good,
then turned him out again to homelessness
at Enoch Powell's 'Water Tower' speech,
And what you viewed was water,
And what you viewed was water...

though Johnson wrote that Africans don't dream,
Oluwale had a dream, followed it
then faded into it, a dream of Britain
Britannia, whose new name makes all tongues sing...
In Ben's time *Britain* meant a tattered mask
repainted by its new and foreign king
to show how borders could just disappear
like dreams or plays, though now this mask's so snug
some wear it and pretend it is their face,
so they're not *E*NP, like SNP
but *B*NP, the xenophobes we chose
to stand for us in Europe's Parliament.
How upside-down, inside-out, back-to-front
yet right for this contrary God's old town.
Saint David, though I know you don't exist,
forgive me while I exit and get pissed.

Via Negativa

IAN DUHIG

Not circumcellion, beggar, gyrovague but Lagos Christian
college boy.

Not abbey-lubber but job-seeker.

Not City of God but Motorway City.

Not office career but casual labour.

· Not Union member but *Last In First Out*.

Not My Father's Mansion but Chapeltown slum. Not *Welcome Brother* but *rent up front*.

Not Empire pilgrim but evicted vagrant.

Not *Ambulare pro Deo* but *Wandering Abroad*. Not *Ave Maria* but Black Maria.

Not demonic visions but brain damage.

Not Church Latin but medical Latin. Not Catechism but
questionnaires. Not Pentecost tongues but echolalia.

Not the African Fathers but *the African Mind*. Not Divine
Spark but ECT.

Not Cloud of Unknowing but Largactil fog.

Not confessional boxes but cardboard boxes. Not the Body
of Christ at Holy Communion but the cold host of a
Leeds moon.

Not *via negativa* but fugue state.

Not River of Life but *Rivers of blood*. Not rosary beads but
bubbles of air.

Not fisher of men but fished from a weir. Not heavenly
throne but pauper's grave. Not heavenly choir but football
chant:

And you shouldn't trust a copper
if your name's Oluwale
and you can't find your way home.

Flooding Back

IAN DUHIG

i.m. David Oluwale

In Ovid's *Metamorphoses* Book VIII,
he hangs fresh wreaths on branches of the trees that Baucis
   and Philemon had become
at the same moment the old couple died.
To save them from the pain of either's loss,
they'd begged this gift from gods they'd taken in when every
   other door was closed on them.
But masked gods walk among us as a test,
for hospitality's a sacred duty
binding all who claim morality;
on their high ground, Baucis and Philemon
were safe in their dilapidated home
when judgement visited the town below,
and neighbours' tears, withheld for homeless gods, now
   swelled a tidal wave that rose and fell
on mansion as on hovel, bank as church;
a flood as levelling as that first great flood
when dead fish perched like scaly birds in trees
or wreaths left by respectful votaries,
while underneath, waves billowed like blown wheat on
   wheatfields yielding only anchor-holds,
as if the Aire became that element
it sounded always destined to become,
a change to take the breath away from men.

Time Come

LINTON KWESI JOHNSON

Linton Kwesi Johnson was the first British poet to include David Oluwale in his work. This poem was written in 1972 and first appeared in his book of poetry titled *Inglan is a Bitch* (Race Today, 1980). A recorded version with the Dennis Bovell Band was included in the album Forces of Victory (Island Records, 1979) and can be heard on YouTube. Johnson is only the second living poet to be published in the Penguin Modern Classics series. This poem is reproduced from *Mi Revalueshanary Fren: Selected Poems* (Penguin Modern Classics, 2002, 2006).

it soon come
it soon come
look out! look out! look out!

fruit soon ripe
fe tek wi bite,
strength soon come
fe wi fling wi mite.

it soon come
it soon come
look out! look out! look out!

wi feel bad
wi look sad
wi smoke weed
an if yu eye sharp,
read de vialence inna wi eye;

wi goin smash de sky wid wi bad bad blood
look out! look out! look out!

    it soon come
    it soon come:
is de shadow walkin behind yu
is I stan-up rite before yu;
    look out!

but it too late now;
I did warn yu.

when yu fling mi inna prison
    I did warn yu
when yu kill Oluwale
    I did warn yu
when yu beat Joshua Francis[2]
    I did warn yu
when yu pick pan de Panthers[3]
    I did warn yu
when yu jack mi up gense di wall
              I didnt bawl,
    but I did warn yu.

now yu si fire burning in mi eye,
smell badness pan mi bret
feel vialence, vialence,
burstin outta mi;
    look out!
it too late now:
I did warn yu.

---

[2] Jamaican worker badly beaten by Brixton police officers in the early 1970s
[3] British Black Power organisation with branches in London. Active in the 1960s and early 1970s

A Letter for Mama Oluwale

ZODWA NYONI

This poem was adapted from the Leeds Young Authors team piece 'Golly Gosh Oluwale Gone,' performed at the opening night of *The Hounding of David Oluwale* at the West Yorkshire Playhouse in 2009. This version was first performed at Britain On Trial: Young Voices Speak Out! at the Carriageworks Theatre, Leeds, on 29th October 2011, organised by Voices that Shake!, Leeds Young Authors, Leeds University MA Activism and Social Change, and a part of the ESRC Festival of Social Science.

Iya mi mama, dear mama
It is early morning and the air
Sits in the palms of the wind and glides
Round the obeche trees, through the fence holes
And teasingly in the flames cooking cassava and okra soup
Iya mi many suns have risen since we last spoke
I miss you, like the soil misses the rains in harmattan
Se e runti?, do you remember
the summer we spent away in Calabar?
I discovered how to make
Toy cars with wire and bottle caps; it constantly rains here iya mi
But nothing grows with nourishment, not even the people
They only seem to grow with stems of resentment and anger
    towards me
I am a weed on their land and they always uprooted me
I am convinced it is Eshu and Anansi,
the tricksters from the elder's tales who trouble me
without reason in the guises of authority

They call me names I do not know and expect me to answer them
They play the games of Ayo but the stones are their fists
And instead of against the ground they hit against me
their games always end with me confined
In their prison or madhouse and them on the other side
Laughing, full pot bellied laughs
Like satisfied hyenas after a hunt
They make a mockery of me.
Iya mi they make a mockery of me
And I fear they have not come alone
In the night I am a disobedient child needing to be punished
Do you remember the stories
of the disobedient children take down to the river bed
left for Ninki Nanka to come for them; Iya mi, it is here
and in the darkness of the night i am scared it will wake
Pull me to the depths of the waters and i will no longer write you
I will no longer tell of the things I have done,
The places I have been and woman, that I love
Iya mi, edakun e wa mu mi, please mama come for me
Because they punish me
For being Oluwale
For needing to sleep at night
For walking along the streets
For living, loving, laughing
They punish me for dancing
to the rhythm of the city
Iya mi, edakun e wa mu mi, please mama come for me
Before I can no-longer come back to you.

David.

from *Aire: a memoir in rivers*

THE BAGGAGE HANDLERS

i.m. David Oluwale

This piece is inspired by river-themed work by writers: Alice Oswald's *Dart* and Ted Hughes' writings about the River Dart.

These extracts of a longer play-length poem were devised as part of a commission from DOMA for the 2013 launch event of the Remember Oluwale charity. The play was performed beside the River Aire, near where David drowned, at the Water Lane memorial garden site in honour of David on the 23rd January 2013 by: Terry, Barry, Owen, Jane, Steve, Andrew, Ruth, Rommi, Ray. Written by Andrew, Paul, Stevie, Hannah, Owen, Barry, Jane, Steve, Jo, Terry, Nico with support and additional text from group co-facilitator and writer, Rommi Smith (www.rommi-smith.co.uk).

The Baggage Handlers is a creative writing drop in for writers and artists living with mental health distress, in Leeds UK. The group meets regularly in Leeds City Centre, to write in celebration of life, personal journeys and stories. Co-facilitated by writer Rommi Smith, (in collaboration with members of the group), the group works to use creative writing as a tool for positive mental health and physical wellbeing.

This extract of the poem-play is dedicated to the memory - not only of David Oluwale (whose life and story are the reason and politic of this work) – but to our dear friend and comrade, Paul Priest, (writer and founder member of The Baggage Handlers), whose spirit and fire sings through these words.

The Baggage Handlers make the tick tock sound in various styles and ways: shouting, whispering, singing, elongating the words, shortening them etc. There is one main speaker. The performers move in, like robots to 'box in' the performer, as though the 'walls' of the institution/ hospital are closing in.

STEVE *speaks*

> The clock on the wall holds ultimate power
> Counting misery by the hour
> Inhumanity in the dock
> Tick tock tick tock in the punishment block

The performers circle

> Never stop our world is at stake
> Marking tea and cigarette breaks
> Spinning like a top
> Count our dismay
> Crawling to a stop
> Day by day by day by day
> Erupting violence
> Deep despair
> Time is the all
> That is always there
>
> ICT stupefied
> The blurring hands cannot be denied
> ECT catatonic state
> You cannot escape time
> It will stop …
> And wait and wait

Time counts for hell
When you are mentally
and emotionally unwell.

*Terry walks on with a tray of pills and hands them out to all the
performers.*

What's their answer?
I tell you, still -

*Performers take pill bottles and shake them to a rhythm.
Everyone holds them aloft so the audience can see them.*

they shake the bottle,
you take the pills,
till you're shaking
the bottle and taking
the pills, til you're shaking
and taking the pills
taking the pills

shaking and taking the pills

Autobiography of the Medication Trolley

TERRY

My ancestor was a wooden horse,
innocent on Troy's hot plain,
deceptive and ambivalent.

I am a dream of science,
restless on a stormy, medieval night,
my mother a witch who must be tamed,
screaming down the hallway
at furious priests.

My cousin is the drinks trolley-
Edinburgh to London,
Hot tea and coffee
crisps and Danish
chocolate and Heineken,
need a receipt mate?

My arrival on the ward is the climax of the day.
They line up like penitents to Mass,
craving forgiveness.
Nurses hand down the Holy Tablets,
(sometimes too the syrup)
and the patients are redeemed.
They go back to doze before Deal or No Deal,
or to their beds to dream of Salvation,
(known as Discharge
in contemporary parlance.)

My ancestor was a wooden horse.
Now I sit on the beige linoleum,
inside me psycho-active warriors
Waiting their chance to subdue
The tiresome barbarians.

ANDREW, *a ghost in Highroyds speaks*

I'm the ghost of here, David – and I think I always were.
Though yer skin's t'opposite hue to what I can see of me now,
I know the pain yer going through.
I were there too – when I was on that side
That electric thing – it does yer brain,

How can yer be people when yer tret like that?
Would never o'wanted me old dog to feel that.
Heck, I wouldn't wish it on anyone,
'cept them that say it has to happen.

Little letters, long words,
they don't need you to understand.
But you know what they're sayin',
You learn a word when it's been done to ya like that.

If my heart still beat it would ache for yer, even bleed.
I'm grateful for the mercy that brought me from this suffering.
But to see it on another is so much worse.
Please man, let me take your place.

A madhouse don't need new martyrs.
Get out the door, take your opportunities –
And you can take my share an' all.

Everyone in the cast repeats the word: tick, until Jane says his 'life away'

his life away, each
Second, minute, every hour and day,
Months through to years, this he must
Pay. His disordered conception of time;
Of an outside world; of the construction
By police of some alleged crimes.

Locked inside the padded cell of his own
Mind. Anaesthetised, sedated, emotionless.
Staring blankly at dark green walls in an
Induced blindness. Heavy limbed, apathetic,
Devoured by a medically inflicted, self
Consuming numbness.

Imprisoned, where you never belonged.
Forced here by cruelty, poverty and civil wrongs.
The bitter cold makes you shake, fingers and
Toes ache, chilblains awaken, itch, burn.

Where is the point of return?

I watch him lay on the hard floor; nothing
Seems real to him. He doesn't feel the fear
a trapped animal would feel. The only thing to look forward
to – is the next meal. Like Pavlov's dog hears the
Ring of the bell, the smell of cabbage combines
With B.O. and piss – in this living hell.

And I know it well.

RUTH

So when they ask me:
who is David Oluwale?
Where is David Oluwale?
What is David Oluwale?

I say:

I am David.
I am David with the sun setting on empire.
I am David with storm clouds filling the Western sky.

Everyone joins in with the I of Ruth's sentence

I am David, a solitary light – extinguished,
but now, rekindled.

Everyone joins in with the I of Andrew's sentence

Andrew turns

ANDREW

I am David
on a cold slab
at St. James' Hospital
I am David of the Black cherry
whose fruit falls to the earth

Terry raises a hand and clenched fist

STEVIE

> I am David
> who fell
> I am David
> who never lived to tell

Barry raises a hand and clenched fist

BARRY

> I am David
> whose story is told through others
> river carries me home
> to my sisters and brothers

Rommi raises a hand as if to touch the stars

ROMMI

> I am David
> with wild hemlock as temptation.
> I am David of the wild flowers.
> I am David, alone, on a corner in Chapeltown.
> I am David who dances for free beneath the sky.

Terry raises a hand, as if to touch the river

TERRY

> he was born of the river
> and who's to say
> maybe the river knew –
> he would return again.

Steve raises a hand and clenched fist

STEVE

> I am David who crossed the sea
> and lived twenty years
> before I was fed to the calm, clear waters
> by angry law enforcers.

Andrew raises a hand and clenched fist

ANDREW

> I am David who dreamed of freedom
> to be dancing on starlight
> on a hard-earned night.
> I am David who could make a brick archway
> turn to a smile.

Andrew shines his torch on the archway, where two people
dance, and into the audience

RUTH

> I am David who returned
> to a small shop doorway
> for vain shelter from the cold.
> A lonely man... my troubled mind

ANDREW

> I am David
> without a chance
> except for the mercy
> of passing strangers.

Barry walks towards the river. Everyone turns to look
  at him. Barry shines his torch on the river and speaks

Postscript: a thought for Olu (David Oluwale)

BARRY

It can take a lifetime to know a man

STEVE

It can take a moment to try.
People are never beyond repair

But if no-one will help
How can anyone know
they are not alone in the world?

BARRY

The river is here.
It was here yesterday.
It has been here for days,
weeks, months, years, centuries,
Aeons. It remembers.

TERRY

It loves to lie here, mouth facing North,
and drink the milk of the clouds.
A heavenly mother rains down –
her natural gift its sustenance and faith.

HANNAH

The trees, plants, roots soak up
the river – in mute adoration.

ANDREW

    It rains.
    The river grows again

TERRY

    It rains. The river says:
    wherever water wakes – I exist.

ROMMI

    And so do you, David.
    The river lit
    by this early evening moon –

All shine their torches from the river up to the moon

    the last milestone, David,
    leading you home.

*Terry plays soft guitar to fade, the performers move
out and into the audience. Music fades.*

A River Was Here

STEVE LUNN

Steve Lunn is a member of The Baggage Handlers. This
poem was written during their project exploring the life
and death of David Oluwale, and was first published at
http://cowbird.com/story/55918/A_River_Was_Here/

Left behind,
Where to go?
How much further? -
Moving slow.
A flight of doves
Could be a sign
I must learn:
Am I a bird
who has crashed and burned?
I, a river – here
[Wait your turn],
Grace will find you
Through the crowds.
Drink the milk
Of the clouds,
Water the horses -
Love and cheer.
I, a river was here.
Love is calling
A heavenly mother
Why resist -
Love your brother.

Fly to Jerusalem -
Or anywhere.
If you were someone else
Would you care?
We have to stare
At the silence
In the forest.
I exist in dreary limits -
but I was born free.

Jo Birdsey, *Oluwale* (2016)

The Remember Oluwale
Writing Prize: Shortlist

POETRY

PROSE

'Aire'
Ian Harker
(Joint Winner)

'Soft Going, Heavy in Places'
Dominic Grace
(Winner)

'Son of the Mother-whose-
children-are-like-fish'
Char March
(Joint Winner)

'The Storyteller'
Anietie Isong
(Runner-Up)

'The Story Has Overtaken Me'
Wes Lee
(Highly Commended)

'Promises (for David
Oluwale)'
Gloria Dawson
(Highly Commended)

'In the Day Room'
Alan Griffith
(Highly Commended)

'In the Cold'
Koyejo Adebakin

'Holler for Oluwale'
Andrew Lambeth

'Touch'
Elizabeth Ottosson

The Remember Oluwale
Writing Prize:
Longlisted Entries

In the Cold

KOYEJO ADEBAKIN

As we turned into Milton Road smoke gushed out of my mouth, partly for frost that has descended upon our town this December, which the Met Office says is the coldest ever, and partly reacting to the imposing concrete structure in front of us. Architects of this six-floor 1970s building didn't leave you in doubt of its importance. It stands tall by the roadside and has a vast frontal car park and a pyramid-shaped war memorial. To register a death or newborn in Harrow, start a business, enter into legal union with a lover, register to vote, make alterations to your property or pay monthly property tax, this is where you come. I, my partner and our four-year-old son are attending one of its several departments on this dusky Harrow afternoon.

I knew this day would come. To be honest, I'd fretted thinking of different scenarios by which it would happen, from that spring evening when — my partner's idea — we'd moved to this London suburb, into a neighbourhood of standalone and semi-detached houses with side garages, of roadside trees within short distances of each other, of endless yellow and brown leaves in autumn and an immaculate greenery in summer. That was five years ago.

Before then, whenever I passed through areas of London that highlight my foreignness, I simply recoil and mimic urban solitude — thumbing pages of Metro, City A.M. or Evening Standard on the Tube, and block out other commuters. On the bus, I'd sit by an upper deck window engaged with buildings, shop neon-lights and car rooftops. And exiting at my stop, like a stream at a tributary, I blend with the familiar: African takeaway menu on shop windows, voices of guys chatting in West-Indies English Creole and West African languages outside the bookmakers' shop, hooded bodies of white working-class kids and Afghani-owned corner shops that allow you groceries on credit.

That is why, settling into a two-bedroom end terrace house in highbrowed Harrow, taking delivery of black faux-leather sofa and ottoman, and installing a plastic slide in the rear garden for our then-crawling infant, and frequenting Italian restaurants on high-streets of Hatch End and Pinner Village, and contracting the local farm to deposit bottles of frothy unpasteurised milk at our door, caused me to daily look out from our leaded bedroom window with anxiety of an impostor. What I didn't know, however, was that when this day would finally come, I wouldn't even find solace in fear.

I saw the blue van when it arrived at 8.26 a.m. I'd shut the front door and was walking out of the end of our cul-de-sac taking our boy, who had just begun Reception in this autumn term, to school. The van driver looked unsure and, pushing his power-window pointed to our front door to ask: "Mate, is that last door Number 13?"

I nodded back, internalising 'LOCKSMITHS' on the body of his van, and hastened my steps behind our son who, without much resistance from the cobbled-stones and patches of ice, had glided fast on his green scooter and disappeared behind a neighbour's car. I pretended today was just another winter's day, or how else could I have coped with this morning's event? I charged myself with usual duty of our son's school-run, and my partner rose early for a ten a.m. hearing at the Watford County Court, to explain that we're yet to secure alternative accommodation, and we'll be destitute with a child if today's eviction went on.

The estate agents' hands were cupped by the sides of his face, peering into the house through the murky kitchen window, when I returned. "I'm Matt," he said. It was the first time I felt shame, today. For spindles missing in the staircase like a child whose front milk-teeth had fallen off. And several days' old unwashed dishes that my partner and I had ignored were in the kitchen sink, be-cause our fingers ached under ice-cold water that ran from the mixer. In the past week, we'd hardly been in credit on the debt repayment gas meter. To keep warm yesterday, in our coats and gloves we gathered in the kitchen and boiled water continuously on the stove, and like a tribe around the fire log summoning their ancestor's ghost, we watched steam rise from the pot and tickled our son as windows of the house fuzzed.

"You've trashed the gaff!" Matt said. The wince on his face betrayed exasperation he tried to hide. I inserted the key he was after into the front door and twisted. "The garden is in a state too!" Matt continued, and stepped into the house after me, taking one cautious step after another on the laminate flooring. He opened the draughty cloakroom to inspect it, and then skirted clutter of luggages and black bin-bags containing our clothes, shoes and our son's toys in the foyer, to go up the stairs, looking closely at stains on the cream polypropylene carpeted staircase as he did, while I made into the living room.

Matt's footsteps continued over my head, and after a short stay up there, he floated back downstairs and into the living room, yet grimacing. As if wondering what his colleague was thinking on the day she rented a house with burnt-wood patio doors and in-built barbecue stand in the garden, to a 'feckless' African migrant.

With the dishevelled state of the house, I would've doubted too that the African occupants moved here in a metallic grey Jaguar, five years ago. And that, keeping up with their neighbours, they'd hired a landscaper to tend their surroundings monthly. That destruction of personality began when, after his third Christmas, their son still hadn't said his first word, and intensified five weeks later with a dawn visit of a UK Border Agency Team. That squalor I see today reflects state of two distressed adult minds, not Africa.

After an age of Matt prancing about the house, my BlackBerry vibrated against my thigh. It had sank into the hem of my charcoal coat, and through the broken seams of my satin pocket. I retrieved it. I took down our family photo after reading the SMS.

"I don't get it," Matt said. He, too, had been informed by a phone-call of the judge's decision, as I was, by my partner's SMS. He stood over the crouched locksmith unscrewing the front-door handle with a drill.

"*Yous* aren't only of our tenants to fall back a couple of months on rent. Gosh, I don't know anyone for who four years of the financial crisis hasn't been challenging. *Buh,* yous are only tenants I'm getting to evict. Didn't you contact Harrow housing department?"

Although we'd just joined London's growing list of homeless people in the season of goodwill, I gave the old keys back to Matt, smiling. For, even in this part of London I didn't appear to him as an impostor, an African whose first language is English — an incongruent individual. But rather, I appeared to him as a Londoner. Matt informed me to get in touch within the next three days to get our stuff from the house, before their maintenance team hired a skip. And he left.

When my partner returned from court, I was in the big park on Headstone Lane near our son's school and she joined me. We perched on a bench fitted near the old timber moated manor house, and oak-interior tithe barn and granary that have stood since medieval England, and now local museum. We sat there for about two hours, waiting for the end of our son's school day, exchanging emotionless stares like the Indian paediatrician at Northwick Park Hospital when she announced results of our son's multi-disciplinary assessment.

At one p.m., our son came out, and I dropped to his eye level, smiling, to shield uncertainties in our lives from him. As usual, looking like an astronaut in his blue fleece-lined padded jacket, gloves and hat, he made no eye contact with me and looked distantly. I lifted his green scooter over my shoulder, to his protestation, and my partner held his book-bag and lunchbox. We walked through Headstone park grounds, nowhere in mind. Our son hit sticks unrhythmically on drums in the children's play-area. Park Maintenance changed dog litter bins, football goalposts bare without nettings, Cricket squares blanketed with orange grid, winter birds chirping in Elm trees. And eventually, we lunged over a tiny stream to join Parkside Way. Notably, walking in the park didn't give me that feeling of calm that briefly dispels my anxieties. What came to mind, instead, was the fox that startles dogwalkers in the park and disappear into the bushes. Homelessness is withering me more in hours, than have years of wanting to belong.

Harrow housing department, Civic 2, is a pink building with watermarks adjacent the concrete grand main-structure. Its interior reeks of damp carpet, and our forlorn faces in the waiting-area replicates the tense ambience of a hallway outside a hospital's operating room, of loved ones waiting to hear good or bad news, or both.

A gentleman at reception passed us a form clipped to a board with a pen attached. The form included 'Child's name' and 'School attended'. My heart pumped violently, and my partner clutched our son's brown hands. He's the reason why we are here, and reason why we hadn't been here before today. It's for his good, we agreed. I handed the filled form back and I was told to listen out for our names. Soon, in a blue-walled cubicle, an interviewer's face, who introduced himself as Adam, appeared in a window.

I'm still unsure if it was our complexion or the way we pronounced "Hello," but Adam's first question was: "Where are you from?"

My partner looked at me. "Nigeria," she replied.

"And Mr...erm..."

"I'm Nigerian too," I said.

"...Your immigration statuses?" asked Adam, dropping his pen to cross his arms and tuck his hands under armpits.

"...I came as a visitor seven years ago... and stayed..." my partner said, hesitantly.

"I'd leave-to-remain... but it was revoked last year," I added, my mouth dried, quickly realising there will be no solace here either.

My partner intervened, "But we've just been evicted and our son here, who is diagnosed with a disability, has nowhere to stay." As if appealing to Adam to save him. I reconciled myself then, to believing that this was the beginning of a long separation from our son.

After writing onto an A4-sized paper, Adam lifted his head, satisfied. "Neither of you have recourse to public funds. I'm afraid there's nothing we can do to help."

"He will be destitute with us," I said, referring to our son playing with the tyres of his scooter, hoping I didn't sound aggressive. And surprised that I'd projected into the future, which I hadn't done in a long time.

I'd riled Adam. He got up and repeated himself, perhaps unsure we could comprehend English, as he spoke slowly this time. "Neither... of... you... have... recourse... to... public... funds..." and left the window. Another name was called in the waiting-area, and allocated our room number.

We're now in the cold beside the war memorial outside the Civic Centre. I'm feeling unworthy to stand with my partner and son. The money left in my partner's bag can only buy one more meal for our boy. Shame is eating me up.

Harrow Central Mosque across the road, its brown bricks and marble facade, consumes my focus. I imagined the dome with crescent moon and star as though a crown on my head. Years of listening to autumn guesstimates by Chancellors of Exchequer Brown, Darling and Osborne don't matter; nor do years of paying council tax, VAT on purchases, obscuring into background of public life, nor my son at present risk. What matters is where I'm from — my origin.

Coppers

RACHEL BOWER

I am more than that stain on the pavement when the moon is blood
but there is no cotton for the likes of me, just shreds

of saturated tissue. I'd like to eat
that thin cardboard cup but I need it to catch coppers.

Do not hate me for magenta hands: they are your hands too.
I hold your eyes for a second, look away, your charity done for the
    day –

you wonder if I hate you, if I will grab an ankle or show you up
and you think about the day your daughter shivered without silk.

Teach her sunburst tarantulas so she can plot her web.
Listen to my story. It is your story. I am you.

They call me mad Melissa and I'm not sure if she's mad but I miss her.
My scalp corrodes with hair scraped tight but it's a little safer this way.

Sometimes I smile my mouth at people to move them on.
You see brown mulch and spats of gum where I normally sit and
    wonder if I'll come back

but I'm looking for the park now on Park Lane and sweet grass to
    chew.
If I lick high gloss will it taste of glacier and lime?

In City Square I stare at bare women, bitter and green
watch warm pigeon feet in their hair and wish them pale eggs.

Give me a blush apple so sweet it reminds my mouth of peach.
Cup my gold leaf bones and sprinkle them with rust.

On Broadway

EMILY BULLOCK

On Broadway he ploughs his shopping cart like Columbus across the seas. Legs wrapped in black plastic, hair plaited with dirt. The Stars and Stripes billow around his shoulders; the tattered flag left over from someone else's party. He keeps his eyes lowered; rescues a rolling Coke from the sidewalk.

Tourists, in bright t-shirts, trot out of his way, and office suits, who pass him every day, pass again. They all bite their lips and hold their breath against the unwashed nightmare of him: redundancy, home repossession.

He shakes the last dregs, and a cigarette butt, from the can before bedding it down in his collection. The hermetically sealed traffic swerves around him. But the hollering horns and the hiss of a thousand yellow sinking taxis doesn't reach him.

His fingertips brush the roped-up bags of treasure. He smiles at the tinkle and crunch of aluminium as the cart bumps over hot tarmac. From the red and white of a Friday Bud to the bright green of a Sunday morning Mountain Dew: all the company he needs. No iPhone app to navigate for him. Google Maps can't plot the route he took all those years before when he first heard the call of the American Dream. He tried to answer with an accent thick as molasses and up-jumbled words. Nobody heard him.

He shouts now, a single syllable warning, as a truck tramples too close. He shields the cart with his body. The flag catches in the updraft and tightens around his neck.

One day, when he is ready, he will swap those cans for crisp bucks and he'll be on his way. Until then he keeps the cart moving; one more sail fluttering against the wind.

Helping with Inquiries

JOHN IRVING CLARKE

The ball he carried had not been chewed by a dog
nor was it marked by being kicked in the park.
He used it to squeeze, that's all.

The knife, they were very interested in the knife.
It opened letters and sometimes sharpened sticks.
But why are you carrying it, son?

An empty packet of ibuprofen he should've thrown away.
Have you taken these?
Have you taken anything else?

A cardboard box which held the medals,
his granddad's stories and *his* dad's too
told in a kitchen on Ellerbeck Lane.

Nights of watching for silhouettes in the sky
and leaking light from windows.
Drones and wailing noises in the head.

Something else he couldn't throw away.

Stephen Lawrence isn't on the National Curriculum

JOSEPHINE CORCORAN

I tuck you in
with long ago and far away,
pull the blanket of *it wasn't us, it wasn't here*
around your heart, although I know
that five inches is 13 centimetres,
that 130 yards would cost a lot
of blood. There'll be Rosa Parks
and Martin Luther King for homework
and someone saying it's good
we teach them that,
but no-one has a map of South-East London,
and today your teacher didn't say his name.
I teach you this: He spelled it with a 'PH'
not a 'V'. In 1993
he was eighteen.
He wanted to be an architect.
He was waiting for a bus.

Signs and Wonders

DAVID CUNDALL

"John, they're here," Emma shouts through my bedroom door, as if I didn't know. I've been up most of the night getting ready for them. I'd told Emma and the others yesterday evening, they tried to reassure me, but I knew it in my bones – my time has come.

"I'm sorry John, they're just doing their job." Emma lives in a squat with three others. They keep a spare room for asylum-seekers. The bedroom door is my last defence. This is so unnecessary – I was at Waterside Court only yesterday. Why not detain me then?

We shared a meal at the house last night. I tried to enjoy it. I was thinking all the time it would be my last with these friends. A single globe artichoke from the allotment was the centrepiece, on a platter all of its own, passed round so each of us could take a few bits, suck out the goodness and say how delicious it was. This was followed by brown rice with nuts, sultanas and home-grown spinach. There's only one growing season here. Potatoes are puny compared to cassava or yam, our harvest here was used up within two months. Unearthing the spuds at the end of last summer, warm soil crumbling away from the tubers, brought tears to my eyes.

After the meal, I borrowed a couple of quid from Emma for a takeaway kebab. She understands my need for meat. Before she went to bed, she advised me to trust in the good forces of the universe. My mother said much the same thing when we exchanged hurried goodbyes at Balogun Market in Lagos five years ago, except 'The Good Lord Will Bless You And His Angels Will Watch Over You,' comes from the language, traditions and capital letters of the Miracle Church of Signs and Wonders International, Inc., of which she is a devout member.

"Open this door!" A man's voice.

I guess they'll take me to Harmondsworth. The authorities won't know yet that I visited my solicitor yesterday, made a statement for a fresh claim – though I don't expect it'll do me any good. I'm texting her.

I should have claimed asylum when I landed. I know that now, but I thought that something would turn up. It did – the cold winter of 2011. By then I had exhausted my options of sleeping on the sofas of third cousins or friends of friends. It isn't good to be too visible; the governor has spies. I was on the streets of London. I hope I will never be that cold, or hungry, again.

My boss, the State Auditor, had set me on to investigating various irregularities in the accounts. It wasn't long before I tracked down some of the missing billions of Naira to one of the governor's slush funds. My boss was trying to decide what to do with this information when his wife was kidnapped. Her driver was shot in both hands. Someone paid a visit to my boss to assure him that the governor was doing everything possible to find her. The visitor mentioned, in passing, that the governor hoped that my boss was not going to find any problems with the accounts. His wife was home, unharmed, within days.

By then I was on a plane to London, with a ticket funded from my savings, before the governor's hoodlums could find me. Please don't ask me how I got the visa.

I have more than enough evidence of a realistic fear of assassination but the authorities here decided this was insufficient. I was trained to deal with budgets, numbers, ledgers – things that add up. I gave these people a straightforward account of what happened, all the evidence that my life was in danger. They gave me a shifting, shuffling, threatening mass of contradictions in return. They remind me of the Ekpo men from my childhood. A secret society who, I was told, might be good and grant your wishes or terrorise you to an early grave on a whim. We never knew their identity; they always wore masks.

"Come on sir, we don't want to break down this door." Another voice, a Yorkshire accent this time. No doubt there'll be more of them; a small posse to cope with a quiet accountant.

I stand back and survey the results of last night's carpentry. There are two planks of wood screwed into the doorframe above and below the level of the handle. I had borrowed a screwdriver and some long screws from the communal toolbox. I didn't use nails, didn't want to disturb my friends.

"We will break this door down if you do not let us in." The Yorkshire voice again, sounding his syllables slowly, as if talking to a child.

"John, this doesn't help your case," pleads Emma.

She's right of course. I don't understand why I spent half the night with the screwdriver, perhaps the fever confused me? It's exhausting work, trying to drive screws into wood without a drill. I tried alternating hands but, by the end of it, both palms were blistered and bleeding. As night slid towards dawn, the pain from my hands, wrists and arms was matched by the ache in my bladder.

The handle of my bedroom door turns. There's a splintering noise.

"Give me five minutes," I say, trying to sound calm, "I need to get dressed."

"OK," says the Yorkshire man, "I'm timing you."

I take off the sweat-drenched boxers and T-shirt, put on my best clothes and go to work on the screws. Unscrewing should be easy, but I'm out of energy, shaking and close to tears. I get into a rhythm of pushing hard to get the screwdriver to hold in the slot of the screw, gasp with the pain from my palm, turn the screw half a turn and repeat. I swap hands between screws. The job is soon done. I stow the planks under the bed. All the exertion sets off a spasm of coughing. I must have got infected in London. I hack and hack and eventually there's a gobbet of phlegm streaked with blood on my tissue. The specialist here in Leeds said it should be improving, but the fevers came back a week past Thursday, as they say here. I had another test and they told me to keep taking the tablets. One of the medications turns everything orange. There's a public health doctor keeping track of me. We haven't met but the name sounds Ghanaian.

I open the door. "Good morning. I apologise for the delay." My heart is thudding, but I'm pleased to hear my voice is calm, even dignified. One of my hands is clenched round the handle of my bag, the other holds a tissue, soaking up the blood.

Two men look at me. They do not smile. "Put the bag down," says the Yorkshire man. He's shorter than me and has a bit of a belly. His colleague is a head taller and looks as cold as February.

"I need it," I say.

"We will bring it," says the tall one. He produces some handcuffs. "What have you got in your other hand?"

"It's bleeding."

"Let me see."

I unfurl both hands slowly. Any movement is painful. I bring my arms upwards and straighten them away from my sides. He crosses himself.

"What happened John?" asks Emma, appearing between them.

"I'm sorry."

"Are you alright?"

I nod in reply. Drops of blood drip from my palms. The tall man has turned even whiter. The handcuffs fall to the floor.

"We should not do this," he says.

"Bloody 'ave to mate," says the Yorkshire man.

"But, but, he has s-s-stigmata," hisses his colleague.

"Come again?"

"Stig-ma-ta," Emma spells it out, "Signs of crucifixion."

"He's a couple of bleeding hands, as far as I can see," says the Yorkshire man. "Nowt special about that." He inspects my hands more closely. "Nasty wounds though, could do with a bandage on those. Blood's making a bit of a mess of yer floor."

I stand there and am just able to get my hand to my mouth as another coughing spasm seizes me. He picks up the handcuffs.

"Let's be having you then, son."

"But I have put in a fresh claim, yesterday. I have a copy in my bag."

"That's what they all say."

"Let me get a dressing for those hands," says Emma.

"Thanks," I say, in unexpected unison with the Yorkshire man. He stares at me. "What's with the orange eyes?" he says.

"I'm on some treatment."

"You infectious?"

I shrug.

Emma returns with a first-aid box. "Can we sit down?" she asks.

"Might as well, love," he says, "take the weight off our feet."

She winces at his 'love', but only says, "let's go to the kitchen."

Emma bathes my palms in warm water, dries them, applies antiseptic, which hurts, then gauze and bandages. During the process she finds out that the officer is called Barry, he has a wife, two children, three grandchildren and an allotment. She has a way with people, and bandages.

"Time to go," says Barry.

"I need to ease myself," I say.

"What?"

"Use the toilet, I haven't been this morning."

"Fair enough," says Barry. "Don't mess us about."

I take time sorting myself out, slowed down by the bandages. As I emerge and offer my wrists to his handcuffs, there's wahala at the front door, everyone talking at once and, above them all, the sound of a woman's voice. Not just any voice, but a strident West African voice, the sort of voice you might hear selling pineapples in a market.

"What next?" sighs Barry, shaking his head. The handcuffs are back by his side.

"Good morning all." A small broad black woman appears, hands on hips. She wears a smile that reaches both ears. Her eyes are framed by purple sparkling spectacles. "Are you John Akpan?" she asks.

I nod.

"Dr Mensah." She raises her eyebrows at the bandages and shakes my forearm with her hand.

"I've heard of you," says Barry.

"I'm sure you have. It's all true," she says. "This man has XDR-TB."

"Sports car?" says Barry, chuckling at his own joke.

"Much more dangerous," she frowns. "Extensively drug-resistant TB. I was hoping never to see it in my patch. We got the test result this morning." She turns to me. "You need to be in hospital Mr Akpan. Now. All your contacts should be screened." She looks round and opens her arms as if blessing everyone.

Emma takes a deep breath, she swallows hard and says nothing.

Dr Mensah ploughs on. "As the Proper Officer under the Public Health Acts, I can trump the UKBA whenever I need to. Mr Akpan is coming with me." She smiles at Barry, who puts the handcuffs in his pocket.

Dr Mensah puts me in an NHS version of solitary confinement. I have a comfortable room under negative pressure, to stop my superbugs infecting anyone else. There are no windows. All the surfaces are hard or shiny. The wall clock doesn't work. At regular intervals, I hear a long sigh, as the room breathes in, sharing my boredom. Each time this happens, I make a point of breathing out. The staff could not be more kind. My friends bring me books. The daily routine is measured by mechanical sighs, medication and meals. I am permanently nauseated, a side effect of the treatment. I contribute what I can to my hoped-for recovery by forcing myself to eat whatever is put in front of me.

They do allow my solicitor to see me. She's found an expert in the UK who is willing to give evidence about the disappeared and the violence of my home state.

"How long?" I ask her, and everyone else.

Nobody knows. Everyone has to wear a mask.

Promises (for David Oluwale)

GLORIA DAWSON

1. SECURITY

I watch myself feeling my way around the city wall. I finger the cracks in the stone until my fingers are the cracks, and I walk, as I walk, two fingers, two thumbs, a mouth, a head, a back, two feet, this mouth that we must take bread through, this same mouth. A mouth, a head, a back, two feet, as the sun comes round. The cracks change with light, water expands as it becomes ice.

The place is incidental, then. I am alone, ice pools spread, I am thought in pool, I am still outside the city, I am asleep, and so I surround and am surrounded. Facing the terror, the throat attack which is only a moment, not a policy, not a good deal of time. A motorway or a wall is worse than a bomb. I am pitiful. Exposure to difficulty has made my hands a little rough. There is snow in the cracks in the wall. How far? Even its compensation is loaded with doubt. For a garden, there has to be an idea, a thought of blooming, power, labour. If paradise is a garden, who waters it? That same mouth. My tread rakes earth. I journey.

2. SOCIAL JUSTICE

In the court waiting area, where there are no windows, a woman shows another a black and white photo. *And there's the leg... just there* – at once I am floating, the gabbling becomes water, and I am unfixed in my own ocean, with my child, and a terrible refusal for it to be subjected to this, this being forced to pay rent, money extorted from the threat of eviction. I was in the room with another woman, older, and her friend, a younger woman, and the duty solicitor. He went out and she began to cry, again, weary and familiar, grinning into tears. He came back in, springy, efficient.

Don't cry, he said, *don't cry, it's good news. The council solicitor has agreed to a suspension and for you to pay £3.60 a week. And you might be eligible for a temporary payment to cover your rent. It's good news, the best possible outcome really! Mind those tears now.* As if she had not been crying for ten months.

My child can be a person from whom money is extorted – this is my fury beginning – but in no country that I can imagine my child living in (my child now) will anyone be prosecuted for letting themselves go hungry. Pay the rent. My child, who is a woman, eats so little that her periods stop. Pay up. *And the judge delivers the best possible outcome* of an extorted £3.60 a week, *that's sensible, you can pay that can't you. Can't you*, says the solicitor and there's a small nod, *Yes your honour, the tenant is agreeable to that.* The judge knows his children will never have their rent extorted and a mind that lives on its nerves and severings like that, a womb on ice; he knows the law inside out, as well as they know grief and perhaps a little better, and he knows that he and his dear ones are always inside and that local government is to tough choices as he is to the safety of his ocean, his lake, his home. *But how can they demand that the child never be left, she can't even leave the house, not even to pop out to get bread... she can't be a mum like that.*

3.   WORK

In the photographs of the Workhouse, which is also additionally named the Infirmary, perhaps because the two buildings sit side by side, sharing an internal wall, there are a group of men who are known as inmates, or so it's written here, or patients, as it's written elsewhere. They work to make the crops grow, or to make themselves better, or a more complete man, or in order that they may eat, or in order that the workhouse can grow and take in more people to be cured, restored to work again, that the city stays in order, that the city can be cured. I sit with them, I am the man with the city's disorder, I am the woman in the crumpled skirt.

People are awful surplus, old men with not even a belt to hold up their trousers, so they must use stolen rope, with not a voice to speak of them, not even to record the crime, not two pieces of paper that agree on what to call them. They are the shape the state needs. Almost. For belonging. Either they aren't sure what to call you or, waste matter, they think that you must have several names. Certain sicknesses for certain times. Are you still sick, they ask each month, and then every six months, tell us how. Can you wash yourself, what work are you able to do then? You're not prone, but we don't know what to do with you, because, you see, you won't tell us what to do with yourself. We haven't invented the workhouse yet. Here we are in our past unpoliced, unpolicied state. Apply a sticking plaster to the surplus until something more robust can be constructed. Something with an inside, an outside, and a shared wall.

4.   PROGRESS

Often there are so many fences, it's surprising not to see one. Out of the gate I go, space winds me. Security fences anticipate attack, rebellion, preformed riots, training exercises. I've trodden fields claggy with the knowledge that the fence could not be climbed and I was on the side where I could be caught. Your whole street does not work in the factory. This street was built for the works. That space at the top of the hill where nothing has been built and something has been demolished. Housing infrastructure is no longer dictated by industrial infrastructure; development is about 'regional growth' and we're segmented, market delineated, an A2 or a C3 shopper. Everything about us is known even though there is so much to know, a city for people so various would either be a single palace or a various mess. Everything about us is used to plan the shops we frequent to buoy The Economy up, the shops that sometimes close without warning so when you go to buy cheap stationery, you trip instead over a grey chasm lying like a joke among the moving shoppers.

An Important Man says he is mystified by that fact that the expansion of jobs in the US and Europe has not resulted in higher wages. Capital is a great mystery, and that mystery of these cities of the North, their fragmentation, their porous suffering. The failure, the inability, the impossibility of planning. The collapse of local government, and the decline of civic architecture; 'good works' have gone the way of 'the works' at the top of the street, where the space is. I have stood at the top of a gasometer and looked out onto the huge plain, of factories, canals, of woods and houses, half in smog and half in green. I have wondered what was this all made for? And why is it still here? Down by the empty mills, it mostly feels like a mistake, a chewed field, a nightmare of someone who woke up in the morning, in any year you'd care to name, who woke and cried and asked God for another dream.

i.m. B.B.

IAN FAIRLEY

I was not born to be a ghost
but now I am the ghost of the machine
that works the lungs the heart the kidneys
of the body that is no longer my body
but the body of the congregation that prays for me

it is the winter of the new day
of my birth when gifts are made
and hands grasped in the other
country of my birth that I left
to live with dogs and talk with djinns
and beat on the door of the house
of exile where still I am refused

my breath is an hydraulic ghost
my voice has drowned in my lungs
the soul between my vertebrae pleads for release
the snow on my lips is supernatural bread
I leave you to think of my sister and mother
I leave you to ask what happened
I leave you to find a home for my cat
I leave you the knowledge that I lived

Summer in Winter

RACHEL J FENTON

They said his mother was a whore; it was the Wombwell way to make sense of a woman who wore white stilettos in all weathers and bleached her hair in nineteen eighty-four. And neighbours said they didn't know how many brothers or sisters he had on account of the kids all being so close in age and looking so similar: boys and girls alike wore tee shirts and trousers. It never seemed to occur to people that he was just poor, like us. But this is all stuff I worked out later, or added on, in hindsight.

I first met him when he came to call on my brother to walk to secondary school; we'd only just woken up when he tapped delicately on the door. My mother had a pan of porridge cooking on the gas hob, summer in winter she called it, and he stood by the stove, his socks on his hands and his hands under his armpits, warming the fine bare gaps between his cuffs. It was February. I realised much too late that his delicacy was an elegant aside of being frozen. I stared at his sockless wet shoes and thought what long ankles he had.

He came for breakfast regularly after that, even though his house was much nearer to school than ours, and to call on my brother meant he increased his journey by almost an hour. He was two years older than me and had mesmerising grey-green-brown eyes that waited for permission to twinkle, the kindest smile, shy and afraid, and his voice came out in a sort of soft breath like an honest whisper. My brother got in with another crowd, however, and he called less often.

It was March when he asked if he could walk me to school. I didn't mind, I had no one else to walk with, no friends of my own, and he didn't really have that much to say, so it wasn't very different from walking to school alone. He pulled a daffodil from the flower bed on the High Street, the stem bent, fractured from the wind; he wasn't being naughty. He asked if I would go out with him. We were already walking together and were outside, I thought, why not. Sap dripped onto our uniforms. Flowers have their own language.

The following day, everyone in his year group made a point of finding me at break to ask if I had kissed him. I ran away.

Twenty years later, on the other side of the world, my neighbour shouted words my daughter was too young to hear. In July, the coldest month of the year in Auckland, I drew my daughter to me, held her face to my fleece.

The Curse of Naples

HELEN FORBES

Grabbing the bag. Dashing past the burning tyres. Skirting round the car on bricks. Jumping over the stinking sewer. Landing on corrugated tin. A starving cat bolting over the crumbling wall.

Behind Lucia, beneath the motorway, a shamble of caravans and shacks, a rabble of lazy men, hungry children, broken mothers. Ahead, her older sister and two cousins. They're smoking and talking. Dresses and boys and gossip. Their bums wiggle and their words come to Lucia. Bold words. Bad words. Her sister stops and waits for her, as do the words. There are always words waiting. You grow and the words become things. Things that happen to you in the night.

The cousins are arguing. Always arguing. The sister is squinting her eyes against the sun, scowling at the boy who scurries past. Holes in his jeans. Bruises on his face. "Run home, loser," the sister shouts. "Your mama is in bed with her brother."

Lucia always gets the bag; the others are too cool to be seen carrying it. One day she'll get rid of it, when the little sister is old enough. Lucia will run ahead then, with the wiggling bums and the bad words. She'll smoke and strut and shout rude things at passing boys. She'll turn every so often and wait for the little sister. And she'll know that the day is coming when the bad words will catch the little sister too.

The others start to run. "Quick, the train's leaving." They're lying, just to make Lucia run with the bag, just so they can laugh. She runs anyway.

As the girls pass through the train carriage, arms creep round handbags, clutching them tight, pulling them in like beloved pets. Soon the air is so heavy that Lucia starts to cough. The cousins argue. The sister stares out the window.

A child, encircled by his mother's arm, is pulled close. He peeps from beneath a perfect fringe, his brown eyes wide and curious. They watch each other for a while, the boy and the girl. A hint of a smile in his eyes. It sparks the hint of a smile in Lucia's, the age-old hatred split for a second by the innocence of childhood. Until the mother sees. Sharp words hissed in the child's ear and he frowns, scowls, sticks his tongue out. Lucia knew it was coming. As she jumps from the train, she gives him and his mother two fingers.

On the platform, a cousin shoves a wallet into her pocket. It came from a tourist with earphones, one hand on the rail, the other holding a map, oblivious to the hatred. Round the corner, they huddle in and count the cash. More than they've seen in weeks.

Heavy, heavy bag. Too heavy for this bright day. Lucia wants to empty it in a bin. They have enough money now, but the stolen notes are too big and crisp and new to have been exchanged for the trinkets in the bag. They must return to the camp with pockets full of small change, grudgingly scraped from the bottom of purses. Handed over carefully, without touching.

The bigger cousin kneels down beside a muddy puddle and beckons. Lucia shakes her head. Not today. It's a day for being clean and bright. But she has no choice. The cousin's fingers drip with mud and it feels so clammy and sad on Lucia's cheeks. Tears would be good, the cousin says; tears on a muddy face could melt a heart of stone. Lucia shakes her head. If the cousin wants tears, let her make her own.

They leave Lucia in a cold underpass, sitting on the bag, her wares set out around her. It doesn't do for the others to hang about. No one feels sorry for a gang of young girls, but one grubby girl alone, with sad eyes and upturned hands, and the tourists can't refuse.

The smaller cousin appears and dumps something on Lucia's lap. A laugh, and she's gone. Lucia is glad she changed into ragged clothes before she came down to the underpass, for this thing does not smell good. A weak sound and Lucia knows it. The camp is crawling with them, kittens that no one wants. This one is cold and shaking, its fur matted and scabbed. One eye is gone, the other thick with pus. From the bag, she takes a red hankie. She wraps the kitten carefully. On her lap, it sleeps, enfolded in the layers of her dirty skirt.

When her pockets are full, Lucia changes and emerges into the sun. Glancing back at the underpass, she wonders how long the little sister will last down there when her time comes. She's wild, the little sister, just like the cousins. Maybe she'll seek out the words for herself, long before they can catch her.

"Come on," the cousins shout. "The beach." As Lucia struggles to keep up with them, she wants to ask her sister to carry the bag. But she might look inside, and throw the kitten in the gutter.

The smell of the sea is strong. It's clean, like their grandmother's laundered sheets. No burning tyres in the camp on Nonna's wash-day; no one would dare. Sometimes Lucia sneaks from her own dirty sleeping bag to Nonna's clean bed. Sometimes a cousin or a sister gets there first.

There are diamonds in the sea and they take Lucia's breath. She can't speak, can't hear the others telling her to start with the family by the steps. There is nothing but the sea. It is whispering as it caresses the sand, diamonds dancing. Whispering her to come. Don't look back.

A hand on her arm. A cousin. A vicious nip. Lucia turns from the water. They push her towards the steps and the picnicking family. See how greedy they are, with their roast chicken and prosciutto, their ciabatta and olive oil. See how rich they must be. Lucia can smell the chicken. It makes her mouth water. The innocent laughter of the two children makes her heart sad. No open sewers outside their bedroom windows. They will not do their homework by the flickering light of the last candle, as the motorway rumbles over their heads. They will never cower in fear while the police tear their homes apart. They will always have light and heat and running water. They will always belong.

It has started. Whispers to the children and they move closer to their parents. Bags and belongings are guarded, zips closed. Their food does not taste so good now, and Lucia is glad.

No one is buying. Above the laughter of playing children, Lucia hears the word. It comes from a young mother, her brown skin shining with oil. Lucia has heard the word before and it didn't sting. Today, it hurts like boiling water poured on a raw wound. Today, she wants to cry out. We were born here, she wants to shout, just like your children. She moves on, a wooden turtle in one hand, a hankie in the other. An older lady takes pity, buys the turtle, almost smiles.

The cousins won't let her stop, though she's been round everyone. Her curse isn't wild enough, one tells her. Her face is too happy, the other says. Her sister says nothing. She's sorry for Lucia, but she won't cross the cousins.

On her second trip around the sunbathers, the scorn is so thick Lucia can taste it. A boy throws a stone. It stings her leg and he laughs. She utters the worst curse she has ever heard, shivering inside as the venom pours from her. The boy laughs again and she realises that the curse meant nothing to him. It was in her grandmother's language, not his. She wouldn't even know how to translate it; perhaps there are no Italian words for such poison.

Lucia turns to find the others gone. They were sitting on the steps at the sea wall when she last looked, as far from the scorn as possible. Have they left her? Perhaps the last train has left too.

Footsteps. Children, braver now that she's alone. Creeping up on her.

Whispering. Mocking. The word.

Scum. Scum. Scum.

And she knows. It doesn't matter where she was born. They will never be the same. She takes a step towards them, spits, and they back away.

From the shore, a cousin calls out. They're paddling in the shallow water, where the sea is etching flames into the sand. Lucia snatches the bag and runs. No one follows.

When she reaches their shoes, discarded on the sand, Lucia looks inside the bag. She kneels and digs a hole with her hands. She places the dead kitten carefully, crosses herself, and scoops the crumbling sand into the hole.

Jeans turned up, she throws off her shoes. The diamonds have merged and the sea is molten silver. She lifts the sparkling water in her hands to wash the mud from her face.

Below the cliff at the end of the bay, the others have clambered up on the rocks. Lucia laughs as she tries to run towards them. Her legs are heavy, her heart so light, as the sea splashes from her and rises in sparkling droplets. She lifts her face to the sun and screams with joy.

They help her up on the rocks. One cousin keeps an eye on their belongings. The others lie flat out. The sun is growing hotter. The tide is coming in and the sea is deeper. Lucia is captivated. Nonna whispered of the sea once, of a different sea, a childhood sea, in the days before she left her home. She cried as she whispered. She should have stayed on the shores of that sea. Stayed where she belonged, where people were all the same. She should have kept her heart to herself, kept it from the wandering gypsy that took her from her home, dragged her from one stinking camp to another and another and another. And left her. Discarded. Scum.

It wasn't always that way, Nonna had whispered. We came from somewhere good. We belonged. One day the sea will take us back; it will take us home.

Home.

The cousins gasp as Lucia leaps from the rocks. As she hits the sea, it sprays up in front of her. Through the broken water, she can see the cousins' shocked faces. It's good to shock the cousins.

Before, the sea had a floor; now it's gone. Lucia slips beneath the waves, water gushing into her nose and mouth. As she struggles, she's aware of her sister beside her. They sink together. Lucia holds her breath, though the cold makes her want to gasp. Her body rises a little and she can see the sun glinting through the shifting waves. In just a moment, her head will clear the water and she will breathe. She will laugh. She raises a hand above the water, reaching for a cousin. There is nothing there, just waves that break on the rocks and force her back down.

Lucia has known pain before, but not like this. Her chest is being crushed by giant boulders. She cannot hold her breath. She gasps and screams, but the rushing water silences her. It burns and tears and paralyses her throat.

Her sister has slipped away. The pain rises and rises. It is new and terrifying and consuming. And she knows. She can't fight this. The struggle is useless. There is no point in trying; there never was.

As the struggle stops, she is filled with calm. The pain slips from her. She watches it sail away on the silver sea, just like Nonna's dreams. Her body is tingling all over, music ringing in her ears. A light so bright it takes the chill from her body and warms her to her heart.

Home. She's going home.

Soft Going, Heavy in Places

DOMINIC GRACE

Is it raining there? I'd say it's soft going, heavy in places over here.
I know how it'll be back over. Throwing cobbler's knives, I bet. Is
the earth soft? I know it is. They say a little rain never hurt no one
but that's not true just like most things people say aren't true. I
think it's time now, though, for truth, for me to speak my truth to
you and you to hear it if you will, if I can ask that. Just about how
things are and how they were and what was and what wasn't and
about the broken chain and the fights and the man I am now. If
you'll hear me.

I'd tell you all of this *grá mo chroí*...and I'd tell you about the
quiet room in the White Rose Centre, that's just near the jacks,
but I know the smell is off of me not from there so I can't use it
as an excuse when I hide away from the rain till they move me on
like they always do and that's me back on the bus into town down
Dewsbury Road, the rain beating on the front window makes
me think of the time when we were young and on the bus from
Abha na Scail up to *Lios Tuathail* with a few bob in our pockets
for the races and me not telling you where the money had come
from but not feeling a bit of guilt over the church's loss, our gain,
and me not knowing how many more pounds would follow that
money on slow horses and quick whiskey, and do you know now
it's the church and me again, all wrapped up with each other like
old flames and me there only a few weeks ago at Christmas for a
free dinner and a bit of warmth and there was an old fella maybe
my age from back over and he sang the sweetest *Sean Nos* with
his eyes all misty like the road over the *Slieve Mish* they were like
a milky blue and I knew he'd been a good looker of a fella once
upon a time, smart too I bet, and my own eyes filled up because
I thought of you and how I was only to be here for a while we

said, enough to make some money but London didn't work out and neither did Birmingham and then up here in Leeds and the coldest winter I've ever known, but I was indoors to sleep then and young and there was company and singing and dancing almost as good as the Galtymore and real fires and hard work with men like myself, hard with the weather and the pickaxe and shovel and there was nothing we couldn't build, the strength on us, and then one by one fellas settled or moved and some went home until there was just a few of us left and the work then was for younger men and I'd heard the news from back home that there was nothing left for me, ah but I should have come anyway, I should have come.

You won't know the song the young fella sang about New York, an ugly fella, I don't remember the name but they play it everywhere at Christmas and I think you're supposed to feel sad but I can't bring myself to feel sad because he's got his colleen even if she's just the same as him, all used up and washed up because some of us are that way and without even the co-pilot and so we just have people we nod to now and then but there's no friends left, lads like Ball o'Muck and Big Tom and Scion Sullivan, and it's the Holy Joes I see more than anyone and these mean well not like that bastard back home, you'll remember him, may he burn in hell the sanctimonious devil always telling me what I would and wouldn't be and who cares if he was right because he was wrong about the main thing and that is my heart was always true but that wouldn't mean a thing to a man like him all incense and nonsense and judging everyone and never being judged himself, dead before anyone knew what he was but I always knew and I think you did too but I don't want to talk about him and I don't really want to talk about me, the me I am now.

I remember the first time I kissed you, girl, and all those years are just a tissue I can rip and be there again and you climbing over the wall at Scanlon's and me on the other side to catch you and I think you had it planned all along because you didn't move as you dropped into my arms just tilted your head a bit and blew those raven curls out your eyes and looked up at me and smiled all shy, like, and then it happened and for me the world shrank to nothing but us and...and we were everything in the universe, if you get my meaning, the rivers, seas, valleys, mountains and oceans and all of that was in the first brush of your lips that I can almost feel if I close my eyes and smell your hair playing hide and seek with your red bonnet. Oh Bridie, girl.

Jesus would this rain ever stop lashing the balls off me and nowhere to get dry without the entry fee of a pint, there's no shops'll tolerate the likes of me for long before the security guards come to move me, blokes I'd have swept aside or knocked down in the years that are lost to me now, all lost, and do you remember when you saw me last when the mother died and I was back over and I couldn't look at you standing there in church with him, and me all fire and sinew and rage back then and for what I don't know only that it's all lost now and I don't remember why it was there to begin with but I extinguished it anyway with the lads at first, pints flowing down and music playing to deafen the heartbroken wildman, and later whiskey with the dwindling and the dwindling dwindled and then just the whiskey and no one left to pretend to be sane for, and it's true that you can forget because I've forgotten nearly everything except the one thing I wanted to.

There are dry places I can go but they're full of me, in every other face it's me, and I've just about had enough of me. My stupid pride that stayed around just that bit too long before going completely almost in one go so I could become who you see now, a wretch I wouldn't have looked twice at before passing by years ago but back when I still had the pride I remembered the letter from the sister saying he'd died, the other one, and that I should give it a while before maybe coming home and looking you up but I'd listened to the teacher reading WB Yeats at school, the only thing I recall listening to without getting a hiding for staring out the windows and too long a sacrifice had done to me what old WB had said it would do and if I could go back to that letter and unrip it, unbin it, reread it, believe it, then things could have been different but I know it's soft bollocks talk to think like that and if I still could I'd pick a fight to teach someone a lesson like I learnt my lesson from WB and my fists like the stone that my heart had become.

There's no need and no point for to tell a lie to you now and after I saw you in the church I came back to England and I've never been back home not even when I got the second letter, and that one from your sister, and I was already living bad back then but the madness came on me then and it wasn't long after that I got the kicking that broke me and the doctors said there's nothing showing up on their machines but I know there's a chain or something inside me and it got broke that day and I haven't been able to fit it together since and all I've had is bad luck, just one thing after another, with losing work and then the place I was biding and since then it's been hard, Bridie, I don't mind telling you but I'll never tell another living soul I've no time for them that weeps for themselves and if I ever do I do it where no one can see me which is easy because the likes of me are invisible if we want to be.

Can you imagine me invisible? Me! Remember us walking down Denny Street or through the Rose Garden in *Tra Li* and every eye on us in our Sunday best and all whispering what a handsome couple we were and we were the finest pair the town had seen and it felt like our whole life story was already written but I don't suppose it was or if it had been and we'd have read it, we'd have laughed like madmen and thrown it on the fire. Everything felt like it would be easy then and all the chapters that should have happened were stolen from our book. No big day, no forever, and no children, not just our own but no children apart. My name dies with me and that's for the best, I suppose, but I think on the children that we never had.

I'm coming home soon. That's why I'm talking so much tonight. I want you to know I'm coming back. The priest has promised me the boat ticket and a lift on the other side. Will it still be raining, do you think? I'm sick past saving, Bridie. I just need to know about the rain. I couldn't stand a frost, and I'm too weak to cleave the hard, frozen ground any more. When I come to join you, we must make of the soft earth our wedding bed.

In the Day Room

ALAN GRIFFITH

There are always jigsaw puzzles to do,
timeless on the shelves under the window,
the pictures perfect on the lids,
a country farmyard, park gardens or dales,
all stone walls, daffodils and clouds,
but the pieces never all the right way up
and always some pieces lost, others
too big or too small, the wrong pattern,
too much sun or the colours too strong,
some from more challenging puzzles
for which the lids are missing, pieces
splitting at the edges or bent out of shape
or the connecting bits torn off,
and ever at your shoulder
a meddler or two, minded to work
on the borders first, and keen to police
where the right ones should go and
discard those they're sure don't belong.

Records

OZ HARDWICK

On the wireless, Desmond Dekker
hits the beat that ties the world
together, easy as black and white,
but your head spins a different tune.

No nightclubs now for you; you fear
the beat of the club in the gloved fist
as you shiver in doorways, listening
to a coarse chorus only you can hear.

After a storm there must be a calm.
Insufficient balm for an all-night DJ
in an all-white world, fighting yourself
unconscious when everyone's gone home.

Until, a skewed accent, radio static
spits you awake. *It's time to shake
that lame tail, darkie.* This one
will run and run, live on Aire

and dead beneath. *Get Back*
is the hit when the river gives you up,
a different beat in the same world,
while all your records are conveniently lost.

Aire

IAN HARKER

Eastgate

There's a change in pressure where a building used to be – memory
of brick
and windows, a spot you come across like dowsing where there
wasn't any rain.
They're demolishing Millgarth. A few years ago David stared it down
from a billboard on the side of the Playhouse and the hair stood up
on the back of my neck.

x

The Dark Arches

Everything smells of water. You can't shout for the water, you
come out smelling
of water, it panned down off the hills and came to this, water
slapping the back
of your throat, the weave of the river against the canal, boxing
clever, fighting shy.

x

The Calls

Friday night in a white teeshirt, straight from work. You won't
    believe how cold it is.
The silt comes from nowhere and you're punchdrunk, river like
    a windscreen,
your shoes are downstream with kicking, you're another pair
    of shoulders.

x

New Briggate

Doorway after doorway. Leave your mark in cardboard, the sag
    of it, the cold
of the plateglass. Everyone wants you here – finger and thumb.
If you won't cooperate, if you won't even try. The footsteps say
    show willing – doorway – shopfront – finger and thumb.

x

Killingbeck

Where water meets earth, a grave filling like a stairwell. The
    dead are the mirror
of the living, all lit up – the living full length, the dead lying
    back, grabbing
at their shadows. Millgarth goes down in a swirl of brickdust –
    cell doors, white tiles, time servers walking on thin air. The
    lights go out. A grave fills with water.

What's that in English?

CLARE IBBERSON-JOHN

What's the word for that in English? The word for that feeling inside?
Leaving because I couldn't stay knowing I couldn't hide
What's the word for that in English, being so tired you can hardly
    breathe
What's the word for that in English? What's the word for rest in
    peace?
Come to me all you who are weary and I will give you rest
What does that mean in English, Miss? I need it for a test.

Deport me back to my boy days I want to be there with friends,
    running by the truck was the best fun, dusty barefoot now play
    time's done
Alone now not after class, I'm running for my life, hiding not a
    child's game
I want to be found by a friend I want to be found with shouts of joy
    "he won the ting again"
I'm lying barely breathing, the sounds of slowing down,
What's the English? What do I say that means waiting to be found?

What the fuck you doing back there you could have fucking died
    you fucking stupid illegal you'll get me fucking fired
Speak English you fucking bastard get out of me fucking way where
    are you, where are you what the fuck you trying to say
Yorkshire, God's own country now fuck off before I lose pay

I want to rest I can't rest I can never truly sleep
What's the English for that Miss? What's the English for rest in
    peace?

The Storyteller

ANIETIE ISONG

My name is Ime. I was born, my mother says, the day soldiers seized power in a bloodless coup. My mother, a storyteller, has been the record keeper, chronicling births, deaths and the history of my family. It is from her mouth that I heard the story of my uncle Joe, from the beginning of his marriage to Yemi, through the drama of his military service, the birth of his children, and the untimely death of his wife.

She is a master storyteller, my mother. But sometimes I worry that stories transmitted orally from one generation to the next, may have been distorted. Why don't we write down our history, instead? I suggest to her one day. Like our neighbour who had written a biography of his father: 'The life and times of Chief Gabriel, Nigeria's first graduate of geophysics.' But my mother is not comfortable converting stories which had been narrated in family gatherings, into written texts.

"You know, writing robs storytelling of its colour," she argues. "It is our nature to talk."

We live close to Evergreen Telephone Talk Centre, a popular business centre. Every day, I see men and women file in and out of the rickety structure with rusted metal roofs. Whenever the customers inside the centre raise their voices: "Why are you not listening to me?" I imagine those on the other end of the phone, defiant, bellowing back: "Why don't you shut up?"

I have never crossed the River Niger, which divides where my late father comes from, in the southern part of Nigeria and Lagos - the western region, where I live. I enjoy eating *amala* - one of the local delicacies in Lagos. I also speak fluent Yoruba, the local language. The day before my 28th birthday, it dawns on me, how long I have been tied to my mother's apron, how long I have lived in Afolabi Junior Street. I make plans to move out, to relocate to Ajah, a suburb of Lagos in the Lekki Peninsula. My friends Edmund, Eze, Tolu and Ogolo have also moved to Ajah. They now live in flats that overlook the Atlantic Ocean.

I find a nice and affordable apartment in the property papers – one of those new ones that claim to have offices in Accra, Pretoria, London and New York. My telephone conversation with the landlord is in the Yoruba language. He is happy that I am a banker.

"I am a retired auditor," he tells me. "I spent thirty five years stalking fraudsters. If I tell you what I unearthed, you will weep for this country. Those big men you see all over the place, their hands have been soiled. Even some so called men of God, are like the devil themselves. We live in a corrupt world, my son. Just open your eyes wide when you are dealing with people."

When he asks if I have attended a banking course in London, I inform him quickly that my office has a well equipped training school in Lagos. We continue bantering until I mention my name – Ime.

"You're Efik?" The landlord's question hits me like a cold wad of spit.

"Sir?"

The man coughs. He murmurs. He sighs.

"Sir…"

"You should have told me you were Efik," the man comments, the congeniality gone from his voice. "You shouldn't have wasted my time. I don't need a non-Yoruba tenant."

Sleep eludes me at night. *I don't need a non-Yoruba tenant!* The landlord's words buzz in my ears like a niggling mosquito. What does he mean that I am non-Yoruba? I speak the language. I live in Lagos. I was born here. Just what does he mean? The church next door doesn't help either. It is one of those nights they have their vigil. Their loud insistent prayers and praise-singing interfere with my thoughts. In the bathroom the following morning, when the cold water hits me, something happens. My mother is having breakfast when I burst into the sitting room.

"I am Efik!" I declare to her.

I do not even realise I am nude. I stand there, in front of her with my penis swinging like a pendulum. My mother screams. The only other time I have heard her scream that way was the day a large snake was found in her bedroom.

"I am finished," she cries. "I am finished o!"

I do not know what to say. My tongue suddenly doesn't have the strength to move. Mama's conclusion is that I have gone mad.

"I have always known that there is a spirit of madness in this family," Mama cries."My Lord, my Lord, why has thou forsaken me?"

Mama immediately seeks spiritual help. She does not take me to the church next door. She throws her wrapper around me and then bundles me inside her old Beetle. She drives, like a crazy woman to Mushin. There, 'Bishop' Mandy of Bethel Freedom Centre attempts to exorcise the devil in me with a broomstick. When I tell him that I am Efik, he laughs and tells me the story of an accountant who used to scream about his mansion in Iceland.

"But I cured him," the man says. "Just like I will cure you."

The 'bishop' believes that the spoken word has the power to produce a magical effect when recited either alone or over magical objects. Every morning, he makes me chant certain words. I spend two weeks and four days in the freedom centre. Does the 'bishop' cure me? I do not know.

"I am Efik."

Those are the words that I carry to my sleep. Those are the words that I utter every morning when I wake up. I have just begun learning the Efik culture. My forefathers learned by apprenticeship – by listening, by repeating what they heard, by mastering proverbs. I begin to listen to my mother's stories. She is pleased that I am interested in learning the Efik language. I learn the times of the day. I learn the Efik mythology. I also learn the meaning of my name – Ime – God's patience. I learn too, of highly accomplished Efik men and women - orally educated characters who often reflected, with intelligence and sophistication, on the situations in which they found themselves involved. I learn of Mary Slessor, the Scottish missionary who came to live among the Efiks. I learn that she successfully fought against the killing of twins.

My mother thinks I am learning fast.

At twenty-eight, I have just discovered myself. In this multiethnic country of mine, a man must have dignity and identity. I am Ime. I was born in Lagos. I speak the Yoruba language. But I am Efik.

Holler for Oluwale

ANDREW LAMBETH

Ola told me about you, back when sus law had us
up against the back alley wall. She was Nigerian too.
The grief that caused.

Nothing like yours, I know. Not that it's a competition.
We all suffer in our way. You rinsing cold blood from your
mouth in a river

you couldn't spit. Not then, anyway. Others, itching to
rinse other injuries. You spit, we spit. Get some air going,
some 'penance'.

My body too got dumped in something like the nearest
ditch. Corridor in my case. So what with the cozzer's fist,
the trick cyclist's

fizzlebed and the chemical cosh in common, my off-pale
sees your blue-black in the going-down dockwater, sees it
but can't hear it in the dark

down past the nightdesk where no papers got kept. Me,
I was south, different bin, but your England mine—ours
to walk our hours off

across grass licked into such English shape we seemed to
scut on lowered eyelids and waterboatmen toes as we
took the therapeutic

air through a hole in the lollipoplady laurel hedge into
dry doorway night. So we're all ears. Say what happened,
who did what—go on, say,

get it out your chest. We'll get it going viral, make apps
to make ringtones of it, run it through tannoys down by
the wharf to warn

people of the danger of not learning lessons. Cough up,
David Oluwale. Spit it out. You'll get a plaque out of it.

The Story Has Overtaken Me

WES LEE

I have remained silent –
it is too hard to tell now,
it's so big it's bigger than me
bigger than I.
I have eaten it as a meal each day
and my stomach is distended
and all my joints are popping. It is in the chambers
of my heart,
it is in my intestines.
I am a mercury fish netted
and that silver lining found in my eye
rolls terrified.

The story has overtaken me
it sparks from my fingers,
I try to press it on the glass of windows –
the people eating inside
with their forks their knives
they cannot see me –
I try to put it in the steam of my breath
draw something in the mist.

Son of the Mother-whose-children-are-like-fish

CHAR MARCH

At 19, the mouth of the Ogun breathes him out,
the Humber inhales him, but it's the Aire
that slithers through his sharp-dressed dances;
his college rejection; his Labour Exchange queue;
that (once Tetley'd) slakes his foundry heat.
Ellerker and Kitching are going white
stomping him through Allport's five stages.
The Loiner rain finds him wandering abroad
in the 'jungle' of Middy Woods, shop doorways,
Armley nick, Millgarth nick, the Dark Arches.
It's Mire Beck that circles his corridor-slur of High Royds
where friends hold him, and the nurse dips his hand
to the water-blue airmail *Owon baba... Owon Yemoja...*
And then it's Stage 5 and the long-stanked Aire holds him
under. But PC Galvin whistle-blows, Phillips writes 'Lame Darkie',
Sandford's 'Smiling David' speaks from British wirelesses,
walls remember graffiti, and when the 30-year-gag coughs out
police charge sheets marked 'Wog', a rush of art and outrage keeps
David alive. Here he is, age 86. And in his garden
we hold him, hear his quick laugh.

Zones of Exclusion

ROB MILES

Where do we reckon
the deadening
starts?

Is it below
the navel, or somewhere
above

the heart?
What test could serve
beyond the neural

byways, the pins
in maps
of connection

or inaction, gathering
where paths
have numbed,

at which points
whole parts of us become
closed down to others?

Touch

ELIZABETH OTTOSSON

Leo

The trees are dense at the bottom of the path, deflecting the weak
sunlight. He trudges between them, wishing he'd worn better shoes.
In the distance, kids are shouting – down by the beck, maybe,
fishing god knows what out of the stream before it joins the river.

The hill isn't steep, but he's puffing as he walks. Should've been in
the gym more recently. Shouldn't have had that fifth pint last night.

Should've come here earlier.

The slope's levelling out; any second now he'll be in the park,
looking down across the city. And at her.

He checks his phone. Six-sixteen p.m., six degrees. How does she
survive?

Thanks to Dad's letter – that stupid fucking letter: far too little
information, far too late – he knows she didn't always sleep
out. There were shelters, squats, soup kitchens, the occasional
Samaritan…she's had help. But it wasn't enough, was it, because…

There she is, a dark outline in the gathering gloom. She has her
back to him; she's wearing some sort of puffy coat. That's good, isn't
it? He pulls his jacket tight.

Downhill those kids are still shrieking. The grass slides down
into the city and the rush hour traffic's shushing along the ring
road. And he is here, teetering back and forth on his slippy loafers,
staring at her.

He can make out her hair, straggling over her shoulders, and
that's about it. She's surrounded by shapes that must be bags, or
maybe duvets. He hopes for duvets.

Should've brought something. A hot drink. But what if it'd been
the wrong thing?

She hasn't moved. He closes his eyes, breathes deeply, and when he looks again she's still there. Not going anywhere.

He steps forward and slides on mud, just as she shifts slightly on the bench. Whatever's on either side of her shifts as well, so she looks like she's in the sea, head bobbing above the waves. Just.

Hunching his shoulders, he turns away and hurries down the hill. It's hard at first, like jogging in water, but then his legs break through the resistance and he's running, slipping in the sludge, feet too close to whatever's on the path, but he doesn't care. He's on his way home, back to Ros, back to a hot shower and a world where this kind of crap doesn't happen.

Janine

Gunna be a nice night tonight. Cloud cover, that's what you need. Keeps in the warmth, blocks out all that…all that air, going right out past our atmosphere to them other planets.

When I was little my granny always talked about the moon. How beautiful it was on those clear nights when you could see its light shining all the way into your back yard.

I don't give a shit about the moon now. 'Part from the fact that it tells me I'd better make sure my head's covered properly. Means cold feet, but that's not so bad. Cold feet's painful, aye, and I've had some nasty stuff go on with 'em over the years. But a cold head's worse. That's when you end up in hospital, if you can get yourself there.

I'm not saying hospital's bad, it's a bloody haven sometimes, but last time I was there I thought I was gunna die, I hurt so much. My chest, you know. I got summat for the pain, on a drip, but they wouldn't give me the good stuff in case…well. I know what they think about people like me.

They gave me a little hit, though. I remember, because it was when I started dreaming about my lad again. I think about him all the time when I'm awake – what he's doing, what kind of job he's at. Whether he's got a girlfriend. I bet he has. I bet he treats her right nice. His dad was right nice to me at the start.

But I don't dream much, don't get that kind of sleep. When I do…you know, if someone touches you in a dream you can feel it? Feel the warmth of them, like more than a touch. Like protection. Like love.

I used to dream about others, too. Not his dad – not for years. But people I knew, a bloke who used to smile at me as he handed over the soup. I never thought he fancied me or owt, but I suppose in your dreams you can hope, can't you? There were others, too. Mostly men, even a copper, although I never thought of him like that. He was a proper policeman, like they're meant to be. Like when you're a little girl and you think they'll come and rescue you. They never did, though. I got meself out of there in the end. Messed up me own life without anyone else's help, thank you very much.

My lad. I can't be arsed with the other stuff these days, but I dream of him. Sometimes he comes and finds me here, but usually we're in some other life, where I take him to school and read to him. Them Harry Potter books I found in the library, and all the others I ate up when I realised what I'd missed. And he might be five, or twelve, or nineteen and bringing home a girl. It doesn't matter. What matters is when he touches me and I feel the love through his skin, going straight for my gut.

Leo

There's a lad who sits by the bridge asking for money. Hunched against the brickwork, a hand curled upwards, revealing the dirt in his palm.

Leo checks his pocket, pulls out a couple of quid, and the lad nods his thanks. A few weeks ago he'd have spoken, but the winter's taken it out of him, or maybe just the exhaustion of being out here, scraping together silver for the hostel. How often does he make enough for a bed?

A nod in return, and Leo hurries over the rise of the bridge. His bus rolls past the crossroads, the number a taunt in the gloom, and he darts around the commuters until he reaches the stop. Puffs as he throws down another two pound coins. It's not worth checking upstairs for a seat, so he presses politely into the crowd ramming the interior, not checking out the people closest to him in case they're bothered by the colour of his skin. Undoing his jacket: a flash of suit always helps.

He never thought about them at all, those ghosts folded into doorways or propping up bridges. Drop a few pennies into an outthrust hand and move on, good deed done. But then Dad died, and the letter...

Now he thinks about them. How did that lad end up on the bridge? What happens to him on nights when he can't get a bed – does he sleep? Wander the city? Get beaten up?

And then her, always her. How she ended up where she is. Why the hell nobody ever did anything. Why nobody ever told him. Why she's still here.

Janine

I dreamt about my lad's dad last night. Not had one of *them* for a while, I can tell you. Woke up all smiley and tingly...until I remembered what it was really like.

Not his fault, what happened. He didn't know how to deal with me. I didn't know how to deal with myself, so it wasn't his fault. He tried.

These days there'd be counselling, I bet – some idiot in a shirt explaining to me why I did all that stuff. Trying to *help*. You know what would've helped? Tying up those fuckers who dragged me up, and chucking 'em in the river. Showing them how it feels when you can't get out, when you're so scared you can't move, can't make a sound, even though you're drowning.

Just say they were wrong. Just say it.

I get 'em up here sometimes, the do-gooders. Usually just after the coppers have been – I mean, how'm I supposed to move all me stuff? Where'm I gunna go? One o' them places full of beds, full of who knows what sort of people, up to who knows what sort of shit?

I'm not letting that happen again. Nobody's ever doing owt like that to me again.

Anyway, I was thinking about my lad's dad. Maybe I picked him 'cos he was so different from everyone I grew up with. I don't mean background – he was from here, same as me. I mean his colour. I thought I might be safe with him, dunno why. I suppose I was for a while. Like I said, we tried.

We got my lad out of it. The best thing I've ever done. The worst was leaving him to his dad when my head went tits up again.

If I concentrate I can still feel him – a hand on me arm, warmth spreading from his body to mine. I can last all day with that feeling: just a touch in a dream.

Leo

It's lighter than the last time he came and the mud has dried into ruts. He thought about bringing coffee, but what if she drinks tea instead? She's from Yorkshire, after all.

Still, he stopped at the cashpoint on his way through town. And he's been thinking since last time. Talking, too, because he finally told Ros what was in that letter, and she took it pretty well. She's a teacher; she's seen plenty of crap.

He's still furious with Dad; not sure if it's for dying so bloody pointlessly, or because of what he never said. Your mam left, he said, and shrugged like that was it. Nothing else, like by the way, she's still around, sleeping on the streets, surviving who knows how. By the way, your mam's alive. You can go and chat to her whenever you want.

He does understand. He doesn't need Ros and all her social skills to explain why Dad never let on. He's spent twenty years dreaming about his mam, wondering whether one day she'd turn up, maybe take him away and show him a different life.

You look like her, Dad said, but it was never a compliment. Something to hang the longing on, maybe, but that was as far as it went.

At the top of the rise, he pauses under the trees. He has a photo of her now, and Ros says he's got her jaw, her eyes. But she won't look like that any longer, and he needs to gather himself, to prepare for what might be waiting for him on that bench.

Branches crack behind him and he jumps, but it's just a jogger, a girl in lycra with a rucksack bouncing against her shoulders. He moves aside, then counts to ten and steps out of the trees.

She's where she was last time, facing the city down below. Does she feel safe up here, away from it all? Or is she just too tired to move?

He peers at her, searching for details. Her hair's longer than in the photograph, but that's not a surprise. She looks quite big, but it's hard to tell with all that padding. He's still glad about the coat.

He lurches forward. She doesn't move, and he wonders, for a horrible moment, if she's dead. Then thinks that at least that would solve everything. Put things back the way they were.

Another step. Another, his trainers gripping the grass firmly, which is good, because he feels like he's about to fall off this hillside. One wrong move and he'll be gone, tumbling away into nothing.

He's about five feet away and she still thinks she's alone. Or else she's dead.

When he breathes in, he can hear it above the wind through the trees. She still doesn't move.

"Mam," he says, and her padded back straightens and then stills.

Remembering Oluwale,
January 2016

HANNAH ROCHE

That year, December played out on Netflix
and Boxing Day stockpiled sandbags like fists,
then it rained for two weeks, then Bowie died.

And my news feed gargled petitions to sign:
a stitch-up, Wisconsin, 2005,
where the police put this man away for life,

this white man, who once set a cat on fire.
But Leeds was as sick as America
and the streets were still muddied by dirty floods:

debris, black marks, stains, foreign muck
forcing whitewash from walls, warm flasks from mosques.
So the Aire strained to spit out my city's crime

from a place stuck between April '69
and Times Square, January, *David* in lights.

Excuse Me for Dancing

DAN STATHERS

There's an arrangement in the dance halls,
an 'excuse me' song for strangers, a chance
to flex your wingtip shoes and crease your three piece suit,
treading carefully around the local lasses who tingle
on the hips of your taboo, and for those three minutes
you feel more than just tolerated,
more than their stowaway or migrant.

If only we could see you then,
not their sorry mess on the slab
dragged from the poisoned river,
your body kicked like a bag,
the contents of your smashed dream;
a comb, a toothbrush, charge sheets
folded neatly into your prayer book:

Remember Oluwale, written on
Yorkshire stone and chanted on the terraces,
Remember Oluwale, clinging to a city for dear life.
Not Good Enough!
Remember Oluwale, young man, shine in his step,
smiles then asks for this dance.

He Remains

CHÉRIE TAYLOR BATTISTE

David's last run with head broken heart strong pushed on
    all our thighs
Carrying The Black Man's Burden and tripping on Darwinian
    ties
Fascist fists downward spiralling his mental twists, then
    filthy push into river Aire
Dirty shame mucky waste and Knostrop final place, no milk
    and honey there
From foundry where he worked right to Middleton Woods
    where like stray dog they left him
You'd think they'd have heard his hounded tears
And in Bridal House doorway where one of them relieved
    himself on bed he slept in
That the mannequins would stand head bowed for years
But in the Market Tavern they did not pause pints down
    with lips not yet wet
And at Millgarth some say to this very day they've still not
    truly heard David yet
But the Golden Owls saw Sergeant Kitching and Inspector
    Ellerker and witnessed the city's shame
They'd watched Enoch's Rivers of Blood slipstream in and
    heard the promises drain
And seen like trade winds mental health policies shift and
    rough-sleeper services drift but none erode the stain
Stow-away regret but neither the river nor owls forget and
    so he remains

Because as he was gathered up by water he was wishing for
wells in our eyes now

Hoping we could see his Lagos skies now

And know him not as Alliwalla or Wog but that Oluwale or
God Comes Home is his name

And write it with the Travyon Martins Bikos and Sarah
Reeds in scorebook of injustice endgames

We're all in same mire simmering with David's fire but Yorkshire
winds gently cultivate space for him and fan his flames

And with the sparks hope flies, and even in the mist of our
sighs he is breathing, he remains

A Friendship Apart

CATHERINE VALLELY

My best friend and I were very much alike and different at the same time. We were both baptised Bernadette but while she had the light breezy name of Bernie, I had to carry the full weight of Bernadette. Bernie was the eldest, so her parents had spent time thinking about the name they'd christen her. Mary, for the Mother of God, Bernadette for the little girl Our Lady had appeared to in Lourdes, and Martina in honour of Saint Martin De Porras. My mother grabbed the name that was going around and put it on me. I was squashed in the middle, and so by the time I was born, my sisters had used up all the usual names of Catherine, Bridget, and Eileen.

Both our fathers had a fondness for the pub, so from a young age the two of us learned to imitate Charlie Chapman's exaggerated facial gestures to communicate silently as we flickered around our houses. We knew if we made noise, our daddies would get cross with our mammies and shout: "What's wrong with you woman. Keep them children quiet or you'll know what's good for ya." Seeing my mother scolding me and my sisters to please my father annoyed me. Sometimes, on the way out, I slammed the front door with all my might. My friend, Bernie, never banged their door.

She lived next door to me in what we would nowadays call an extended family –Bernie's parents, Nan, the grandmother and her uncle Martin. One great summer, Martin built a grotto at their gable end. My uncle built a turf shed in ours. All the kids on the road spent the summer helping Martin build the Grotto. We gathered rocks for the cave-like arch where Our Lady was placed. There was no trouble getting the Mother of God because Masie, Bernie's mother, went to Knock, a place Our Lady had appeared in long before she went to Lourdes or Fatima. She bought the biggest statue she could find.

The Virgin was alone for a while, with no little girl kneeling in front. A crowd of us kids took turns visiting her because we knew she was lonely, so we were delighted when Martin found a 'Bernadette' for the Grotto. Mr. Murphy, who was the real road-sweep, used to get holidays in summer. While he was off, the Council gave the brush and shovel and cart to Martin. Part of his job was to clean the Fair Green after the Carnival people and the fun-fair attractions had gone. Among the rubbish left behind, Martin found a broken Pinocchio doll. We ran behind him as he carried it home under his arm and were dying to help him cut the long nose shorter. He waved us away. The wobbly blade shivered as he sawed. "It would be more in yeer line to go and find some clothes for Saint Bernadette and if ye don't keep away, a few of yeer fingers will be dropping there on top of the sawdust." Bernie borrowed Nan's black skirt that was hanging on the line. I got my grandmother's shawl and someone else found a headscarf in their house. We tied the scarf, French style, at the back of the stick neck. The gang of us went to the dump and poked around. We were lucky, and found a pair of broken rosary beads. Martin draped them around Pinocchio's hands. Our Saint Bernadette was ten times better than the one up in the convent.

Bernie's house was the loveliest on the street. In the backyard, Martin made a cement path, decorated with broken pieces of delft and china that we collected for him. The pattern was of the four hands of cards – aces, spades, hearts and diamonds – which Martin designed and set in the cement. Our garden was full of rows of spuds, cabbage, lettuce and carrots. Bernie's kitchen was a chapel, full of religious statues with night lights in front of them, warm and cosy even when the range wasn't lit. Martin de Porras was the favourite saint. Masie always asked him for help with the rent money. In our house, there was a picture of the Sacred Heart. The tinkers swore by it when they were lying. "Mrs Kelly, as sure as God is in that picture looking down on me, I swear to you it's not your own hen I'm trying to sell you." We said the rosary under Him each night, kneeling on the cold, hard floor, my mother's sharp eyes on me in case I'd fidget.

I wanted to live in Bernie's house full of colour and have Masie as my mother. She knew how to comb my hair into ringlets and not plaits like my mother. I would fish-open my lips while she applied lipstick, then I'd smack them shut, like she showed me, before blotting them with newspaper. While she pencilled in a beauty spot under my eye, she told me stories about Glasgow. People would come up and ask for her autograph, mistaking her for Liz Taylor. She was a real Galway girl – her hair was black and her eyes were blue. My mother's eyes were blue too, but the bare blue of the sky when it's stripped naked of clouds. Masie's were like the wild violets that grow in the countryside.

Bernie was strange. Any chance she got, she was in our house talking to my mother while I was in her house, listening to Masie talk about Teddy Boys and gang fights. Every year the family went to Scotland for a few months to pick potatoes. If Masie hadn't told me, I would never have known what a knuckle fist was. She said the Irish had to be careful not to get beaten up, because there used to be gangs waiting for them, swinging bike chains, and telling them to get back to their own country. So when Mammy said the trimming at the end of the rosary, for the missionary priests and nuns, I used to change it, in my own mind, for Masie and the others from the road. Fewer and fewer of the families that went 'prate picking' were now returning home. Empty houses outnumbered the lived-in ones. One year, Bernie's family didn't return home. After the potato-picking season finished, they got the train to Manchester, where Martin had moved to, instead of the boat back to Ireland.

A few years later, some French nuns came to the school looking for vocations. My mother put my name down and I was sent off to France. I disappointed her. Instead of becoming a nun, I married a French boy who admired my beauty spot. He was Jewish, which I thought was great. My kids wouldn't have to say the rosary.

Bernie and I kept in contact by letter. We didn't get to each other's weddings, so that first year that we managed to get home for holidays, she brought the pictures of her and Nigel on their wedding day. I didn't have photos, but I had a baby in my arms. My mother wasn't too pleased my little baby girl had come so soon.

From then on, Bernie and I spent our summer holidays at home. The second year I had two kids, the third three, the fourth four. Pierre and I called a halt at the fifth child. I couldn't stop them coming out of me, while Bernie couldn't get one into her. Her arms were empty, while mine were always full of a wriggling bundle. She told us the doctor said there was nothing wrong. Herself and Nigel just needed to buy a bottle of sherry and relax. After ten years, the sherry worked. Little Nigel came into the world. She adored her baby and never let him out of her arms. Even when the little lad was five, she was still carrying him around on her hip. Then she never came home again. The wheelchair was the reason, too much of a hassle.

She stopped writing when her husband died of cancer. Mine died too, when my youngest was twelve. Life and death got in the way of our friendship.

Four years ago, I returned to Ireland for good. A month later a letter arrived. It was from Bernie. I phoned her. She flew over to visit. Nearly forty years had passed since we saw each other. Sitting there on the sofa, we couldn't have been more different – me dolled up in the latest fashion and her plain and sensibly clad, just like Mammy used to be. My mother had stayed in Bernie's life. 'Mrs Kelly's Cakes' was what she called her bakery. It became so well known, she ended up having two bakeries in Manchester. Masie, her mother, had guided my life too. My interest in makeup had helped me earn my living as a beauty therapist. We spoke long.

"Bernadette, do you remember the day the whole school went to see the film The Robe?"

"How could anyone forget that day? We were so excited, Bernie."

"A matinee on a school day!"

"Ah, the nuns didn't mind us missing class once we saw the Roman soldier save his soul. They got us all lined up in two and marched us down to Ocean."

"I nearly missed it."

"Why?"

"Daddy drank the money. So no one would know, I said to Sister

Reyes, 'An bfuil cead orm dul amach' and snuck away to the toilet."

"What?"

"Bernadette, your mother went looking for me and found me sitting on the stone floor of toilets, crying my heart out."

"Bernie, I could never go into those toilets because of the stinking smell."

It turned out that not only did Bernie see Victor Mature looking at Jesus on the Cross, Mammy also gave her the price of a choc ice, something she never gave me.

I saw my friend a few more times before I got a call from Maiseen, her younger sister. I flew to Manchester. Bernie's house was full of relatives. They were still arriving from different parts of England and Scotland. I was the only one from Ireland. When her cousins arrived from London, I thought I had stepped into the set of *EastEnders*. A swarm of big-breasted blondes with cockney accents buzzed around the tea pot. Maiseen told them who I was as though I was known to them. I was. Their mothers and grandmothers never stopped talking about the road they had left in the sixties and the people who lived on it.

Knowing that most of the people at the wake were bilingual, I wasn't nervous about blabbering away in our way of talking. Maiseen told everyone how I used to make her sister laugh when I told her stories about the tea dances and my romantic life. Bernie loved to know I hadn't changed since I was small and was still up to devilment. Hearing about my goings-on kept her entertained, as in the last few years Bernie's health had deteriorated and she had to sell her business. Bernie's son, Nigel, like my kids, had grown up. He had a life of his own and had moved into a care unit. She knew it was better for him to be independent. However, like all mothers when their children go away, she missed him. Bernie knew I miss my children too, but she understood I wanted to live in Ireland for a few years to recapture what emigration had taken from us. With everyone listening, I reeled off yarns about my mad life in Ireland. It turned into a wake like the ones at home when we were small. All the auld songs from The Waltons radio programme were sung in English and Scottish accents. While the words *'Twas the curse of emigration, laid you low my Noreen Bawn*' drifted through the room, Maiseen brought me upstairs to the landing. The banister where they found Bernie hanging was spotless.

The Weight of a Life

STEPHEN WHITING

They say the ocean has no memory,
but rivers
they never forget.

The weight of a life
 – a tonne of bricks and feathers –
drops down to the sea bed,
depositing fragments of itself
amongst shingle, stone and sediment

displacing a body of water
that, elsewhere,
becomes the salty tears of the sea.

Notes on contributors

KOYEJO ADEBAKIN

Koyejo Adebakin was born in Lagos — Nigeria. He has a diploma from the British College of Journalism, and lives in London with his partner and their special needs son. He is currently working on a novel.

KESTER ASPDEN

Kester Aspden was born in 1968 in Toronto but was raised in Yorkshire. He was educated at Lancaster University and Fitzwilliam College, Cambridge. He taught the history of crime, policing and punishment at the University of Leeds and was a visiting fellow at the Centre for Criminology, University of Oxford. His book *Nationality: Wog, The Hounding of David Oluwale* won the Crime Writers' Association Gold Dagger for Non-Fiction in 2008 and was adapted for the stage by Oladipo Agboluaje, opening at the West Yorkshire Playhouse and touring a number of important venues. He is currently working on a memoir of his youth and a book about the salsa scene he found when living in Havana (2011-14). He is now living in Russia where his wife is BBC Moscow Correspondent.

THE BAGGAGE HANDLERS

The Baggage Handlers is a creative writing drop in for writers and artists living with mental health distress, in Leeds UK. The group meets regularly in Leeds City Centre, to write in celebration of life, personal journeys and stories. Co-facilitated by writer Rommi Smith, (in collaboration with members of the group), the group works to use creative writing as a tool for positive mental health and physical wellbeing.

JO BIRDSEY

Jo Birdsey is a 24 (going-on-64) year old BA English (Goldsmiths, 2012) graduate living in London and currently working in online content and social media. His degree hang-ups include a strong interest in contemporary and world poetry, particularly work which shines a light on the intersections between culture and memory. Through professional and personal projects he is exploring graphic design, with a view to moving into publishing.

RACHEL BOWER

Rachel Bower is an Artist in Residence at Bank Street Arts (Sheffield) and runs Verse Matters: a monthly feminist arts night. She is also a Cheney Cultural Fellow at the University of Leeds.

SJ BRADLEY

SJ Bradley is a writer from Leeds, UK. Her short fiction has been published in the US and UK, including in *New Willesden Short Stories 7*. Her novel, *Brick Mother*, is published by Dead Ink Books. She is one of the organizing party behind the non-profit literary social Fictions of Every Kind, and the instigator and programmer of the Northern Short Story Festival. She lives in Leeds with her husband and cat. www.sjbradleybooks.blogspot.com

EMILY BULLOCK

Emily Bullock won the Bristol Short Story Prize with her story 'My Girl', which was also broadcast on BBC Radio 4. Her memoir piece 'No One Plays Boxing' was shortlisted for the Fish International Publishing Prize 2013 and her short story 'Zoom' was longlisted for the Bath Short Story Award 2014. She has an MA in Creative Writing from the University of East Anglia and completed her PhD at the Open University, where she also teaches Creative Writing. Her debut novel, *The Longest Fight*, was published by Myriad in February 2015.

JOHN IRVING CLARKE

Since resigning his full-time teaching position John has been facing up to the "terrifying freedom to write." His self-published novel, *Who the Hell is Ricky Bell?* was well-received and it has given him the confidence to produce two further manuscripts of novels and a number of short stories. He has been published in Scribble magazine and short-listed in the Writers' and Artists' Short Story competition 2015 as well as being the overall winner of the Magic Oxygen competition 2016. John is co-organiser of the Red Shed Readings in Wakefield and he tutors an adult creative writing group as well as leading writing workshops for schools and writing groups.

JOSEPHINE CORCORAN

Josephine Corcoran is a poet, playwright, short story writer and blogger. Her pamphlet *The Misplaced House* was published by tall-lighthouse in November 2014.

DAVID CUNDALL

David Cundall is a recycled paediatrician living in Leeds. He is learning the craft at the Leeds Writers Circle. He volunteers with Leeds Asylum Seekers Support Network (LASSN) and coordinates the Nigeria Health Care Project. His first novel - *Walls of Fire* - about African exiles in Leeds is, like them, looking for a home.

GLORIA DAWSON

Gloria Dawson writes plays, performance, essays and poetry. Her interests are the relationship between political organising and lived experience, the politics of death, cities.

IAN DUHIG (JUDGE)

Former homelessness worker Ian Duhig's seventh book *The Blind Roadmaker* is a Poetry Book Society 2016 Spring Recommendation. A Cholmondelely Award recipient and Fellow of the Royal Society of Literature, Duhig is a joint winner of a Shirley Jackson Award for short stories, the only twice outright winner of the National Poetry Competition and has three times been shortlisted for the TS Eliot Prize. He is currently working on a project involving refugees suffering from PTSD and their therapists.

IAN FAIRLEY

Ian Fairley was born in Edinburgh and has lived in Leeds since the 1980s, where he now works as a teacher and psychotherapist. His poem 'i.m. B.B.' was written in response to the death of Bahram Bairmi, an Iranian asylum seeker, in 2013.

MAX FARRAR

Max Farrar is Secretary to the Board of the David Oluwale Memorial Association. He responded to Caryl Phillips' suggestion that there should be a memorial for David in the city of Leeds by setting up a working party while he was Professor for Community Engagement at Leeds Metropolitan (now Beckett) University. For about 20 years he worked in a social work centre, in adult and community education, at the Harehills and Chapeltown Law Centre, at the Runnymede Trust and as a freelance writer and photographer. For another 20 years he worked in Higher Education, completing a PhD sociology thesis, 27 years after he started it, on the social movements, mainly led by black people, in Chapeltown, Leeds. His journalism, photos, book chapters and journal articles have been widely published and his books include *The Struggle for 'Community'* (Edwin Mellen 2002) and the co-edited *Islam in the West: Key Issues in Multiculturalism* (Palgrave 2012). He is currently co-writing a book about the British revolutionary organisation *Big Flame*. www.maxfarrar.org.uk

RACHEL J FENTON

Rachel J Fenton was born in South Yorkshire and currently lives in Auckland. Her unpublished novel *Some Things the English* was a finalist in the 2014 Dundee International Book Prize. She is co-editor of the women's comics anthology *Three Words* (Beatnik).

HELEN FORBES

Helen Forbes is an author and a lawyer based in the Scottish Highlands. She specialises in social welfare law. As a writer, she often focusses on marginalised communities. Several of her short stories have been published, and her debut novel *In the Shadow of the Hill* was published last year.

DOMINIC GRACE

Dominic Grace is a writer based in South Leeds.

ALAN GRIFFITH

Alan Griffith was born in Bangor, North Wales into a Welsh speaking family. He was brought up and educated in Ontario, Canada and in the early 60s returned to the UK to study architecture at the Architectural Association School in London. His career includes work as an architect, as an executive director in the construction industry, and as a full-time college lecturer. He now concentrates on writing poetry which draws on a wide range of interests and experiences and diverse literary influences. He is married, with a son and three daughters and lives near Lewes in East Sussex.

IAN HARKER

Ian Harker was born and lives in Leeds. His work has appeared in *The North*, *Agenda*, *Other Poetry*, and *Stand*. In 2014 he was shortlisted for the Bridport, Troubadour and Guernsey International prizes, and in 2015 he was Highly Commended in the Bridport. A Winner of Templar's Book & Pamphlet competition, his debut *The End of the Sky* was published in 2015.

OZ HARDWICK

Oz Hardwick is a poet, academic, photographer, music journalist, and stubborn would-be musician. He particularly enjoys collaborating with other artists in a variety of media, and has spent so much time out of his comfort zone that he's forgotten where it was.

CLARE IBBERSON-JOHN

Clare Ibberson-John was born in Holmfirth in Yorkshire, left at 18 to return at 50 via London, Hong Kong and St Vincent & the Grenadines. She is a mother, teacher and progress coach who performs poetry. She also is a director of Callaloo Carnival Arts UK.

ANIETIE ISONG

Anietie has lived in Nigeria and the UK. His short stories have been published in many journals and broadcast on radio. In 2009, his story 'Devotion' was included in an anthology of short stories edited by Catherine O' Flynn, published to mark the 10th anniversary of Tindal Street Press. Anietie has won some writing awards including the Commonwealth Short Story prize and the Olaudah Equiano Prize for Fiction. His first novel is forthcoming from Jacaranda Books.

LINTON KWESI JOHNSON

Linton Kwesi Johnson was born in 1952 in Chapelton, Clarendon, Jamaica. He came to London in 1963, went to Tulse Hill secondary school and later studied Sociology at Goldsmiths' College,

University of London. He was a member of the Black Panthers, and developed his work with Rasta Love, a group of poets and drummers. In 1977 he was awarded a C Day Lewis Fellowship, becoming the writer-in-residence for Lambeth. He then worked at the Keskidee Centre, the first home of Black theatre and art. In 1974 *Race Today* published Johnson's first collection of poetry, Voices of the Living and the Dead. He has had four more books published and in 2002 became only the second living poet and the first black poet to have his work included in Penguin's Modern Classics series, under the title *Mi Revalueshanary Fren: Selected Poems.* Johnson's first album, Dread Beat An Blood was released in 1978, and since then he has released 14 more albums, including LKJ Live in Paris in 2004, a CD and DVD celebrating his 25th anniversary as a reggae recording artist. Linton Kwesi Johnson has been running his own record label, LKJ Records, since 1981. He has worked in journalism and still regularly tours around the world with the Dennis Bovell Dub Band. He is also a Trustee of the George Padmore Institute. In 2003 Johnson was bestowed with an honorary fellowship from his alma mater, Goldsmiths College.

ANDREW LAMBETH

Andrew Lambeth, the child of an alcoholic lesbian couple (when homosexuality was illegal), largely grew up in hospitals and convalescent homes until, aged twelve, he was finally sent to school. Expelled four years later, he lived rough, was incarcerated in a mental hospital, then an experimental clinic for disturbed adolescents, then a succession of squats, until going to art school as a mature student. After that he had an award-winning career working in publishing, branding, television, and university education. He never outlines both strands of his life experience in the same statement.

MARINA LEWYCKA (JUDGE)

Marina Lewycka was born in a refugee camp in Germany, and now lives in Sheffield. Her first novel, *A Short History of Tractors in Ukrainian* (2005), published when she was 58 years old, sold a million copies in thirty five languages. She has since written three more novels and her fifth, *The Lubetkin Legacy*, was published in May 2016.

STEVE LUNN

Steve Lunn is from Bradford and has been writing for about five years. He is a member of the Baggage Handlers, a Leeds based group that raises awareness and promotes good mental health. He believes that poetry is a massive nourishing resource and his involvement in the Oluwale project has taught him that we have to strive for truth and a better future.

WES LEE

Originally from the UK, Wes Lee is currently based in New Zealand. Her chapbook of short fiction, *Cowboy Genes*, was published by Grist Books at the University of Huddersfield in 2014. She was the 2010 recipient of The BNZ Katherine Mansfield Literary Award, and has won a number of awards for her writing. Her poems have appeared in *The London Magazine*, *Magma*, *Poetry London*, *Riptide*, *The Stony Thursday Book*, *Westerly*, *Underneath: The University of Canberra Vice-Chancellor's Poetry Prize Anthology*, and *The Best New British and Irish Poets 2016* (Eyewear Publishing). She has work forthcoming in *Elbow Room* and *Shibboleth & other stories* (Margaret River Press).

CHAR MARCH

Char March is an award-winning poet, playwright and fiction writer who has had five poetry collections published, six BBC Radio 4 plays broadcast, and seven stage plays produced. She lived in Leeds, working on disability equality and anti-racism for 15 years, and as Writer-in-Residence for Leeds Hospitals. She really valued the opportunity to write about David, and to do more research into his life.

ROB MILES

Rob Miles is from Devon and lives in Yorkshire. He has taught Spanish language and culture at the universities of Leeds, Portsmouth and Hull. His poetry has appeared in publications such as *Ambit*, *Orbis*, *The Interpreter's House*, *Obsessed with Pipework*, *South Bank Poetry*, *Angle*, *Lunar Poetry*, *The Garden* (OWF Press) and *The Anthology of Age* (The Emma Press). He's won competitions including the Philip Larkin Society Prize (2014). Other poems have been placed, commended or shortlisted in competitions including the Bridport, Wenlock, York and Ilkley literature festivals, Live Canon, the Poetry on the Lake Silver Wyvern, the Gregory O'Donoghue, and three times in the National Poetry Competition.

SAI MURRAY

Sai Murray was born in Pontefract of Bajan/Afrikan/English heritage. In 2015 he was lead writer on Virtual Migrants' touring production *Continent Chop Chop* - a theatrical performance combining poetry, music and digital media that addressed issues of migration, racism, austerity and climate justice. In a former life Sai worked in advertising – clean for over 16 years he now works with grassroots organisations such as Voices that Shake! and PARCOE (Pan-Afrikan Reparations Coalition in Europe). Through Liquorice

Fish he has designed, edited and published several books/resources including: *No Condition Is Permanent: 19 Poets on Climate Justice and Change* (2010); *Abeng Soundings: A Timeline of Anti-Slavery Resistance* (2008); *Cross Community Dialogue Facilitation Toolkit* (2007). Sai's debut poetry collection, *Ad-liberation*, was published in 2013.

ZODWA NYONI

Zodwa is a playwright and poet. She was announced as the 2014 Writer-in-Residence at the West Yorkshire Playhouse via the Channel 4 Playwrights' Scheme. She has previously been Apprentice Poet-in-Residence at Ilkely Literature Festival (2013), Leeds Kirkgate Market (2012) and Writer-in-Residence at I Love West Leeds Festival (2010). She is currently under commission at the Tricycle Theatre, is part of the Manchester Royal Exchange New Stages Writing Initiative and is participating in the Eclipse Theatre Revolution Mix development scheme. She is also part of Creative England's iWrite Regional New Voices Initiative. www.zodwanyoni.com

ELIZABETH OTTOSSON

Elizabeth Ottosson is a writer and translator who has recently relocated to Yorkshire after a decade of living in London and Australia. She is currently working on two novels, one young adult and one literary fiction.

CARYL PHILLIPS (JUDGE)

Caryl Phillips grew up in Leeds and is the author of numerous books of non-fiction and fiction. His awards include the Commonwealth Writers Prize, the James Tait Black Memorial Prize, a Guggenheim Fellowship, and the PEN Open Book Award. His latest novel, *The Lost Child*, was published in 2015. http://carylphillips.com

HANNAH ROCHE

Hannah Roche is completing a PhD at the University of Leeds, where she teaches a module on Poetry: Reading and Interpretation. Hannah's own poetry has been published in *TRIVIA: Voices of Feminism and The Feminist Wire*. In 2013, Hannah was named a winner in the Tiny Owl Publishing Napkin Story competition. Her entry appeared on napkins in bars and cafes across Leeds, Brisbane, and Toronto, and on the Leeds Big Bookend blog. Hannah lives in her hometown of Keighley with her partner and their two lovely cats.

DAN STATHERS

Dan is a poet from Kingsbridge, South Devon. He has studied creative writing at the Open University, and more recently, The University of Edinburgh through online learning. He enjoys walking his Border Terrier across local fields and also playing football with friends.

CHÉRIE TAYLOR BATTISTE

Chérie Taylor Battiste is of Jamaican, Cuban and Bajan heritage and grew up in Leeds. Her first creative explorations began with writing poetry and then acting at Leeds Youth Theatre. After a move to London and a degree in African Studies from SOAS, she worked in TV research specialising in Africa, later gaining a place on an accelerated progress scheme. She made the shift to in front of camera and began acting on stage and screen, then won the Norman Beaton Fellowship at BBC Radio Drama. Throughout, she has worked with hard-to-reach young people, addressing difficult issues, through drama and film. After becoming a parent, she returned to Leeds, working as a Creative Agent with Cape UK. She has written and contributed to articles on 'Race' and 'Identity' in The Times and The Voice and recently had a piece published in the anthology, *Tangled Roots*, edited by Katy Massey. Chérie is currently working on new poems on the themes of "Otherness, Social Identity and Self."

CATHERINE VALLELY

Catherine Vallely was born in the West of Ireland. Like so many Irish, she had to emigrate when she finished school. After years of living in London she went to Madrid. She studied Spanish Literature and History and lived through exciting times after Franco's death. A few years ago she returned to Ireland to write.

STEPHEN WHITING

Stephen Whiting is a first year PhD student in the School of English at the University of Leeds. He is a recipient of a '110 University of Leeds Anniversary Research Scholarship' and is completing research on representations of masculine anxiety in late Victorian and modernist literature.